¡Viva el Español!

¿QUÉ TAL?

TESTING PROGRAM

Blackline Masters

Stanley W. Connell

Martha Lucía Torres

Test Designers

Jean D'Arcy Maculaitis

Testing Specialist and Consultant

National Textbook Company
a division of *NTC Publishing Group* • Lincolnwood, Illinois USA

Acknowledgments

The publisher would like to thank the students from Holy Cross School, Rumson, New Jersey, and Our Lady of Perpetual Help School, Highlands, New Jersey, who participated in the pilot test for the *¡Viva el español!* testing program. Thanks also to Dr. Kay Hampares, an internationally renowned expert on the Spanish language and culture, who worked on a pilot experiment in Florida, and to Dr. Jean D'Arcy Maculaitis, a second-language teaching and testing specialist, who conducted the pilot studies.

To the Teacher:

The blackline masters in this book are designed to be photocopied for classroom use only.

Published by National Textbook Company,
a division of NTC Publishing Group
4255 West Touhy Avenue
Lincolnwood (Chicago), Illinois 60646–1975 U.S.A.

Manufactured in the United States of America.

67890VL987654321

CONTENTS

STUDENT TESTS (BLACKLINE MASTERS)

INTRODUCTION

Assessment and evaluation of progress in acquiring a second language play an important part in sustaining students' enthusiasm for language learning, and offer you vital feedback necessary for tailoring your teaching to the needs of individual learners. In second-language learning, because students are constantly being asked to produce responses or react to communicative stimuli, there are frequent opportunities for assessment. However, because of the nature of communication and language production, there are different strategies required for assessment and evaluation. The *¡Viva el español!* program offers you frequent, creative opportunities and ideas for carrying out these vital functions.

Types of Assessment

Assessment in second-language learning needs to operate at a number of different levels, because of the many layers of skills and proficiencies that are being acquired, and that thus need to be assessed and evaluated. The types of assessment fall into three major categories: proficiency, achievement, and prochievement. Furthermore, each of these categories can be assessed through both formal and informal means.

Proficiency Assessment

Since the goal of our language teaching is to develop communicative proficiency in students, we must find ways to assess that proficiency. Proficiency assessment seeks to determine what students can do with the language they've been acquiring, and to what extent they can transfer that language into real-life settings that require them to both receive and give information—the act of communication. The emphasis in proficiency assessment is on performance.

There is, however, a "slippery" quality to communication that can make assessment difficult at times. There is not always a "right" answer. For example, there may be countless ways in which a student could respond to a given question or situation, each of which is appropriate. Students may give you answers you don't expect, ones that may take you by surprise, but that still respond directly to the question or situation you've posed. Students may also give responses that are imperfect on a structural or fluency level, but that nevertheless communicate a message that is understandable and appropriate to the requirements of the setting. Proficiency must be looked at in a very global, holistic way. You must constantly ask yourself the question, "Did I understand the message the student was trying to convey?"—and you must remain open and flexible in assessing what your students produce.

You should be aware that proficiency assessment can be very time-consuming, because it requires interaction with individual students or groups of students. For this reason, you may want to spread your assessments out over the entire course of the lesson, working your way through the class. Don't worry that some students will have had more opportunity to prepare for the assessment because they've had additional days of instruction. Language proficiency is not delineated with clear milestones, but is instead an evolutionary, holistic process that does not change dramatically from one day to the next.

Achievement Assessment

Achievement assessment looks at what students know, rather than at what they can do. Unlike proficiency assessment, achievement testing generally has answers that are right or wrong, and is relatively objective. It requires students to demonstrate retention of previously learned content material. In the case of language learning, achievement assessment can tell you whether students have learned specific vocabulary items, for example, or whether they know accurate endings for a verb or an adjective. As such, it is much easier to set objectives and to evaluate progress in this area. Historically, this sort of assessment has been the mainstay of language testing. However, as our goals have changed, achievement testing has taken on less importance. It remains, however, an important part of the overall assessment of student progress.

Prochievement Assessment

Prochievement is a word that has been coined to describe a type of assessment that combines characteristics of both proficiency and achievement testing. It asks students to demonstrate what they know in a meaningful context. Where traditional achievement testing has asked students to respond to isolated items, prochievement testing ties the items together in some sort of situation. You are still asking students to tell you what they know, and there are still right and wrong answers, but you come much closer to simulating communicative use of language. Prochievement assessment may also allow students to respond within a *range* of correct answers—i.e., there might be two or three acceptable responses to an item, but still there is an objectively "right" way of answering. Many of the activities and exercises in the student book follow this model, and lend themselves to assessment opportunities.

Formal vs. Informal Assessment

Each of the categories listed above can be assessed either formally or informally. In the case of formal assessment, students generally should be made aware that they are being assessed, and also be given some opportunity to prepare. It is important to give formal assessments regularly, though not so frequently that they become burdensome to you or your students. Formal assessments tend to create a great deal of anxiety in many students, and while valuable, may in some cases actually hinder the learning process. You should try to help the students understand your goals in assessing them, and make efforts to lower the stress surrounding this sort of testing. Avoid comparing students directly. Create an atmosphere in which individual students see formal testing as something between you and them, designed to help them, rather than to rank them. Formal assessment should usually result in some sort of feedback to the learner concerning performance so that the assessment does not serve as an end in itself, but rather as a tool for aiding the learner in understanding and improving. Suggestions for scoring or otherwise quantifying performance on formal assessments are discussed later in this article.

Informal assessments can be entirely spontaneous, and may be carried out even without the students' awareness. This sort of assessment does not necessarily result in a score or quantifiable outcome, but will still provide much valuable information for both you and your students. Informal assessment should take place as frequently as practical. It may be as simple as taking note of individual, pair, or group oral performance on an activity as you walk around the room, or as you read over written activities, or look over drawings and posters that arise out of an activity. It might also be more intentional, coming at the end of a presentation or sequence of practice and taking the form of a special set of questions that you ask students to respond to or a brief task that you ask them to perform. Virtually any activity in the text will lend itself to informal assessment.

Assessment Strategies

There is virtually no limit to the strategies that can be used in evaluation of language proficiency and achievement. In fact, it could be argued that anytime students produce language, you have an occasion for assessment and evaluation. Each teacher will need to find his or her preferred strategies and techniques based on individual teaching goals and requirements. However, there are some general principles and strategies that will assist you in finding creative solutions for your assessment needs.

"Assessment Opportunity" Helps

Throughout the *Annotated Teacher's Editions* of *¡Viva el español!* you will find numerous suggestions labeled as "Assessment Opportunities." These appear in the Unit Plans section at the front of each book and in the on-page annotations for the student pages. As you read through them, you will find creative suggestions for using the material in the student book, or in some way going beyond it, to find out what your students are capable of, both in terms of proficiency and achievement. In many cases, we suggest ways to vary items from an exercise that students have just been working on. We also offer ideas for linking the practice to real-life events that your students can relate to. We might suggest a game that will use the vocabulary students are learning, or we might give you some questions to ask to elicit particular vocabulary items or structures. Here are just a few examples:

- Ask students to borrow something from a classmate. Have them display on their desks the borrowed item plus one that is their own. Circulate around the classroom, choosing one item of the two on a student's desk, and asking, **¿De quién es?**

- Call out the names of teachers in your school. Have students respond by stating the subject each one teaches.

- State the following situations in English and ask students to tell you what they would say, using an appropriate **tener** expression: 1. It's 99° outside and the air conditioner is broken. (**Tengo calor.**) etc.

- Have students write the answers to three items of their choosing from Ex. B. Let them exchange papers and correct one another's answers.

You should not look at the "Assessment Opportunities" as the only occasions for evaluation. Look at them as ideas, and glean from them strategies that you can apply in other settings.

One-on-One Assessment

Particularly with younger learners, it can be difficult to find time to isolate yourself with one student to perform one-on-one evaluation. It would be ideal to find ways to do this that would afford some measure of interaction with a single student while still allowing you to maintain control over the class as a whole. This will most often occur while the class is working on a task that requires some quiet time, such as working on a writing project. Call students over to a corner of the room with you one at a time, or stand next to their desks and talk quietly with them. A few times a year, you might arrange "special project" days to allow yourself the opportunity for formal assessment, planning to spend two or four minutes with each student, perhaps over the course of two days. Some teachers have also had success with calling students at home, or working with them at lunch or recess periods, or having them record responses on cassettes that the teacher then listens to outside of class.

In practice, much of your one-on-one evaluation will need to take place "on the fly," as you call on individual students to respond, or as you look over a student's written work. Be careful to give all students opportunities for responding to you individually. It is very easy for extremely verbal or extroverted students to dominate in a second-language class where the emphasis is on communication. Introverted students or those struggling with the language will need some special opportunities to interact with you without fear of embarrassment.

Group Assessment

Group assessment is most easily conducted by observing and monitoring activity while the group is performing a task. Be sure to circulate from group to group. As much as possible, you should avoid interfering in the process, allowing students to interact with one another and correct one another. Evaluate students on their participation in the overall process, as well as on their individual contributions. A second assessment opportunity then exists when the product of the task is presented to the class. The *Entre amigos* and *¡A divertirnos!* activities throughout the program provide excellent opportunities for assessing group performance.

Portfolio Assessment

A superb technique for evaluation over time is afforded by portfolio assessment. By having students create portfolios of written work and projects, you end up with a series of "snapshots" of progress that can demonstrate for you and for the student what has been achieved over time. Furthermore, you have a product that can be revised, expanded, and improved by the student as new language is acquired, allowing you to compare new production with the benchmark of the original. Portfolios are also useful for motivating and involving parents in the learning process as they review what their children have been doing.

Many of the *Entre amigos* and *¡A divertirnos!* activities call for students to produce written work, drawings, posters, greeting cards, etc., all of which can be used to create a portfolio. In many cases, the *Entre amigos* practice will even ask students to go back and add to work done for earlier activities, refining or supplementing. You will also find a number of suggestions for student-created Big Books that would lend themselves well to this sort of assessment.

Peer Assessment

When treated sensitively, peer assessment can be an extremely effective tool. Because so many of the activities in the *¡Viva el español!* program are designed for pair and group work, students quickly become used to working with partners, and become comfortable with being assessed by a peer. Among other ways, this can be accomplished by having partners look over one another's work and make editing changes or corrections, by having students prepare short quizzes for one another, or by having a student listen to another student and note down the information he or she hears, and then check it with the person who gave the information. You might ask students to call one another at home in the evening and share information in Spanish. The next day, they can compare what they heard with what the other student thinks was said, and report on the accuracy of the communication. You can also give students checklists of objectives and other criteria for evaluating an activity, and ask them to evaluate the work of their pair or group based on those criteria.

It is important that students understand clearly from the outset that no harshness or unkindness will be tolerated when assessing or correcting their classmates. You will need to create a climate of trust and a sense of classroom community that will minimize the sometimes critical nature of early adolescents.

Self-Assessment

Students benefit when they learn that evaluation is not entirely the teacher's responsibility, and when they learn the value of assessing their own work. Portfolios, mentioned above, are excellent vehicles for teaching the art of critical review of one's own efforts. When quizzes are given, you might provide answer keys on overhead transparencies and ask students to check their own work. You could also provide checklists of objectives before an activity begins and have students rate themselves on how they attain the objectives at the end of the practice. Use the list of objectives on the first page of each student unit as one such checklist. Just before the unit test, ask students to read over the objectives that were set out and ask themselves if they can do each of those things, now that they've gone through the unit. If they find there are things they don't know how to do, they should report this to you so you have an opportunity for reteaching. Self-assessment comes more easily to some students than to others, and will require some practice.

Evaluation and Scoring

While some assessment is entirely informal and requires no quantification, there is still a need for scoring or tracking your evaluations. Particularly with formal assessment, you probably have district or state requirements for reporting an evaluation. Even informal assessments can lose their value for you if you do not record them in some way. There are a number of means of scoring or otherwise recording evaluations. The Testing Program that supplements the series has its own scoring system. Below are some ideas for scoring the other assessments you carry out in class. No matter what system you use, however, we sometimes have a tendency to look at the scores as a means of ranking learners, of proving what they don't know. Evaluation is much more useful when we look at it as an indicator of what students *do* know.

Achievement Evaluations

Achievement and prochievement evaluations are the easiest to score. Because items are objectively right or wrong, you can readily assign point values and keep track of them in a grade book. If you wish to record results of informal prochievement or achievement assessments, you might consider making simple tick-marks beside students' names in your grade book or on index cards to indicate successful responses. These can be tallied weekly and assigned a value. If you are not opposed to the idea of tokens, you might keep a supply of paper money or plastic tokens at hand. Each time students respond correctly, hand them one of the tokens. At the end of the week, they can turn the tokens in, and you can record a score based on the number of tokens.

Proficiency Evaluations

Proficiency evaluation can be tricky, given the subjective nature of language and communication, the virtually infinite number of responses that can be given in many situations, and the fact that communication can occur even when a response is flawed. If there is not a right answer, how can we score performance? To effectively evaluate proficiency, we need to look at a larger set of criteria. One such set could look like this:

- Did the student complete the communicative task?

- Was the message that was conveyed appropriate?

- How creative was the response?

- Was the response linguistically accurate?

- Did the student find ways to express ideas in spite of language limits?

- Did the student perform at ability level?

- Was progress demonstrated?

These lists of criteria could vary according to your personal goals and preferences. Once a set of criteria is established, a rating scale can be created. Obviously, not every one of the criteria is as important to communication as the others. This then calls for a weighted scale which gives more points to those factors that most affect communication, or that combines factors while still giving the greatest weight to communication. A simple scale might look like this:

Score	Performance
5	Excellent communication, almost no errors
4	Communicated well, but with noticeable errors
3	Communicated fairly well, but with many noticeable errors
2	Response understandable, but grossly erroneous
1	Practically incomprehensible
0	No response

The *¡Viva el Español!* Testing Program

A formal, self-contained assessment program accompanies each of the three textbooks in the *¡Viva el español!* series. For each level the Testing Program includes the following components:

- Testing Program blackline master book containing a detailed description of the program, suggestions and instructions for testing, blackline masters of the tests, an answer key for all written and oral tests, a complete tapescript of the audio Test Cassette, and a Student Progress Chart.

- Test Cassette with listening-comprehension activities corresponding to the oral testing sections in the Testing Program.

The components have been designed bearing in mind that students react most favorably to materials that are appealing and applicable to real conversation and that you, as a teacher, need testing materials that are pedagogically sound and easy to prepare and score.

Evaluation Techniques

The evaluation techniques and design of the *¡Viva el español!* Testing Program are compatible with the Natural Approach and Total Physical Response, approaches that stress the use of interesting and relevant materials, comprehensible input, and intense observation and involvement from students. The design of the Testing Program will help you create a nonthreatening testing environment in your classroom—an environment that allows sufficient success to encourage low to average achievers, yet stimulates high achievers and students who are gifted in second-language learning.

Test Types and Objectives

The *¡Viva el español!* Testing Program features two types of tests: (1) a Placement Test to be administered at the beginning of the year and (2) Unit Tests.

Placement Test

At the beginning of the school year, your students will fall into one of the following categories:

1. Absolute beginners

2. Novices (as defined by the ACTFL Proficiency Guidelines)

3. Students with three years of Spanish, using the *¡Viva el español!* Learning Systems

4. Students with some prior knowledge of Spanish from academic or real-life experience

The Placement Test is designed to measure the language proficiency of students in groups 2, 3, and 4, giving you an accurate evaluation of each individual's current level of competence in Spanish. Since the instructional materials in the textbooks have been designed to accommodate all of the student groups listed above, the Placement Test makes no pass/fail distinctions. The test results, however, will provide scores that will enable you to compare your students' abilities and determine your teaching strategies. The Placement Test consists of a series of short subtests for evaluating your students' language skills (listening, speaking, reading, and writing) and their mastery of the elements of language (pronunciation, grammatical structure, and vocabulary). (For your information, the descriptions of proficiency for speaking, listening, reading, and writing at the Novice and Intermediate levels can be found in the *Resource Section* of the *Annotated Teacher's Edition*.)

Unit Tests

Besides the Placement Test, there are 14–17 Unit Tests in each package, including 10–12 individual unit tests, 2–3 review tests, a mid-year test, and an end-of-year test. The Unit Tests fully cover the skills and elements taught in the textbook and accurately reflect the content of the program. While the main purpose of the Unit Tests is to help you evaluate your students' progress in mastering the textbook materials, the tests can also serve as effective review activities when you return them and discuss them with your classes. The key goal of the testing program is to teach communication in context—not as an intellectual exercise nor as a reward or punishment. In a sense, the tests become another instructional tool in helping your students develop and refine their skills.

Conducting the Tests

Conducting classroom tests can resemble a balancing act in which you strive to preserve a nonthreatening atmosphere while you maintain students' enthusiasm for learning Spanish. The following key features of the Testing Program will help you achieve this goal:

- The familiar format of the Achievement Tests will build your students' confidence because students will recognize item types and pictures from their textbooks.

- The open, uncluttered appearance of the test pages, with a limited number of test items on each, enhances readability. Your students will feel a sense of accomplishment as they complete the pages in relatively short periods of time.

- The fact that the tests are not speed tests lessens student stress. Students have no need to "beat the clock" to finish a particular section.

In keeping with the concept of promoting mastery for all students, tests are not excessively "hard," but they do contain items at various levels of difficulty so that all students will be challenged. Suggested time limits for the tests are generous (20–30 minutes) because the tests are essentially power tests, rather than speed tests. As power tests, they generally contain fewer, relatively challenging items and allow students sufficient time to complete the entire test—as opposed to speed tests, which usually feature a large number of relatively easy items but do not allow students time to finish. The technique of having students exchange test papers and score them immediately in class is recommended. By reviewing tests right after taking them, students receive immediate feedback on their errors and have a chance to master materials not yet learned. The *¡Viva el español!* textbook series tests are designed for easy correction, and they feature useful, authentic sentences suitable for oral exercises.

Test-Item Types

The *¡Viva el español!* Testing Program features an imaginative variety of test item types, including recall and recognition items. Your students will be neither surprised nor confused by unfamiliar item formats because the testing program employs the same general concepts and item types as those found in the textbook and workbook. The tests will enable you to quantify objectively your students' language skills and levels of linguistic competence, using a variety of written and oral item types that include, among others, fill-ins (letter, word, phrase, sentence); cloze items; multiple choice; true or false; matching; dictations; placing elements in logical order, or sequencing; rejoinders; naming objects; and circling words, phrases, and drawings.

Item formats used with the audio Test Cassette are largely multiple choice, true or false, and dictations, the latter progressively sequenced from letter (in the optional Part D of Section 3) to word to phrase to complete sentence fill-ins. These items assess recognition of sounds, as well as students' ability to understand words, phrases, brief sentences, and segments of conversations.

Each test section in the unit and review tests is classified according to degree of difficulty, using the following symbols:

- ○ Lowest level of difficulty
- ◑ Average level of difficulty
- ● Highest level of difficulty

The symbols indicating degree of difficulty of the test parts are found only in the Answer Key; thus, students are generally not aware that they are working with items at a specific level of difficulty. The optional, starred extra-credit items always represent the highest level of difficulty and are designed to challenge your most advanced students.

Test Content

Each test consists of three sections:

- **Section 1** is made up of lexical items based on all the active vocabulary students learn in the *¡Hablemos!* and *¿Cómo lo dices?* sections of a regular unit. These lexical items are tested in context, without resorting to English translations.

- **Section 2** consists of structural items covering all of the grammar taught in the *¿Cómo lo dices?* sections in each regular unit of the student textbook. Items are presented in meaningful contexts that will appeal to the students' imagination, sense of humor, and interests.

- **Section 3** contains listening comprehension items, made up of Parts A, B, C, and D, as follows:

  A. Listening comprehension. Students hear a brief conversation followed by five multiple-choice or true / false items, measuring students' understanding of these spoken materials.
  B. Dictation *(Dictado)*. Students listen to Spanish sentences, each repeated twice, and write the missing words and sentences.
  C. Part C, the extra-credit section, consists of five complete sentences, and features an occasional word beyond the lexicon presented in the text. This is done purposely, to give students the chance to discover how—especially with a "phonetic" language like Spanish—spelling can be deduced from sound.
  D. Sound-symbol relationships. In this optional section, students hear words and either write missing vowels or consonants or identify simple stress and intonation patterns.

For every test, Part A, Part B, and Part D are recorded on the audio Test Cassette by native speakers of Spanish. Part C has been designed to be administered by the teacher or an assistant, thus providing the students additional experience in comprehending a variety of speakers.

Placement and End-of-Year Tests

The Placement Test and the End-of-Year Test are purposely similar in form and content. In fact, section by section and item by item, these two tests are analogous with regard to form, content, and level of difficulty. This means that Placement Test scores will have real meaning in determining with precision your students' ability levels relative to the course objectives. The only deviation from this analogous structuring is the teacher-administered Speaking Section, which is found at the end of the Placement Test but not included in the End-of-Year Test. Because of the enormous amount of classroom time required to administer objective, one-on-one speaking tests, the most practical method for measuring your students' speaking ability is on an informal day-by-day basis. However, to guide you in assessing students' speaking skills at the beginning of your academic year, a brief Speaking Section has been included to supplement the other Placement Test results. In this *Testing Program* book, the Speaking Section may be found in the "Oral Test Tapescript and Guide" (see page T-26).

Administering and Scoring the Tests

Administering the Tests

The Testing Program components (blackline master book and audio Test Cassette) contain all the materials you will need for administering the tests. The only exception is the Speaking Section at the end of the Placement Test (see "Oral Test Tapescript and Guide") for which you may need classroom items and other visual aids.

Each test part includes simple written directions to the students and one or two model test items (with occasional exceptions).

For Sections 1 and 2, it is recommended that you read the instructions aloud and complete the model test item or items with the students. This will ensure that students understand clearly what they are to do and gain confidence that this item is a familiar type. By reading the directions and doing the model together, you will guarantee three factors that significantly contribute to a test's validity: clear directions, specification of the material tested, and familiarity with the test-taking technique.

Scoring the Tests

The *¡Viva el español!* Testing Program permits you to analyze test scores accurately and to give your students sufficient feedback in the form of meaningful numerical grades and positive learning reinforcement. The scores are not designed to be punitive; rather, they serve as markers for past achievement and as points of reference for further improvement. All tests allow for a separate oral achievement subscore. The Placement Test Answer Key includes guidelines for interpreting student scores to determine level of proficiency.

A Student Progress Chart is provided in the Testing Program blackline master book. On this chart, you can record your students' test scores, your informal assessment comments, and notes on individuals' strengths, as well as specific language skills that need improvement.

Because all test items are objective, the tests can be corrected quickly and easily by teachers, aides, or the students themselves. Almost all test items count one point each and can be scored on a simple all-or-nothing basis. Exceptions to this scoring are the dictation items in Parts B and C of the Oral sections of all tests. A suggested procedure for scoring these items follows:

Part B: single-word fill-ins (one point per word)

- 0.5 point off for each word that is misspelled, but recognizable

- 1 point off for each word left blank or not recognizable

Part B: complete-sentence fill-ins (two points per sentence)

- 0.5 point off for each word misspelled or left blank

- 0.5 point off for "small" errors (capitalization, punctuation) to a maximum of 1 point off per sentence for this type of error, no matter how many

- 2 points off is the maximum to be deducted from any sentence, no matter how many errors.

Part C: complete-sentence fill-ins (one extra-credit point per sentence)

Note: Score these sentences exactly like the complete-sentence fill-ins in Part B; however, because the items in Part C have a lesser point value, divide the total score for this part by two.

Your final step in the scoring process will be to convert your students' raw scores to numerical or letter grades. As scores accumulate on the Student Progress Charts and the Composite Score Chart, you can convert them at any point using the mathematics required to match them to your institution's grading system.

TEST SPECIFICATIONS

On the following pages are charts of the specifications for Sections 1, 2, and 3 of the tests.

Section 1*

Test	Words Tested	Functions	Skills	Item Types	Points
Placement	falda, nariz, pies, atlética, enfermera, ropero, cuarto de baño, lavaplatos, plancha, fritos, leche, nadie, sandía, zanahorias, quita	functions in Unidad 1 through Unidad 12	reading, writing	matching, matching-completion, sentence completion	15
Unidad 1	la boca, el brazo, la cabeza, la cintura, el codo, los dedos, la mano, la pierna, el pie, la rodilla, la ceja, el ojo, la oreja, la nariz, la mejilla	identifying, and naming parts of the body	reading, writing	matching, labeling	15
Unidad 2	una blusa, una camisa, una chaqueta, una falda, unos pantalones, un vestido, el impermeable, la camiseta, el traje de bano, los zapatos, el abrigo, las botas, grande, mediana, pequeña	naming and describing articles of clothing	reading, writing	matching-completion, sentence completion, labeling	15

---

* Vocabulary tested is limited to the active vocabulary that is listed in the Scope and Sequence Chart of the *Annotated Teacher's Edition* of the textbook. This is the vocabulary presented in the *¡Hablemos!* and *¿Cómo lo dices?* sections of the regular units of the textbook.

Test	Words Tested	Functions	Skills	Item Types	Points
Unidad 3	alta, baja, débil, fuerte, grueso, cómica, popular, generoso, atlética, tímido, simpático, impaciente, lacio, ondulado, rizado	telling about physical and personality traits of people	reading, writing	matching-completion, sentence completion	15
Repaso: Unidades 1–3	pantalones, débil, popular, feo, espalda, baño, oreja, dientes, camisa, rizado	review of functions in Unidad 1 through Unidad 3	reading, writing	matching-completion, sentence completion	10
Unidad 4	el balcón, el buzón, las escaleras, el garaje, el jardín, el patio, el techo, cocina, comedor, cuarto de baño, despacho, sala, dormitorio, dentro, fuera	identifying and naming parts and rooms of a house	reading, writing	labeling, matching-completion, sentence completion	15
Unidad 5	alfombra, videocasetera, tocador, estante, mesita de noche, cortinas, lámpara, retrato, sofá, televisor, sillón, equipo de sonido, espejo, cama, almohada, ropero, cartel, teléfono	naming and telling location of bedroom and living-room furnishings	reading, writing	matching, multiple-choice, sentence completion	15
Unidad 6	el abrelatas, la batidora eléctrica, la estufa, la licuadora, el horno, el horno de microondas, el lavaplatos, la bombilla, caja, bol, grifo, cajón, refrigerador, lata, tostador	identifying and naming kitchen appliances and furnishings	reading, writing	labeling, sentence completion, question/answer	15
Repaso: Unidades 4–6	cocina, estante, estufa, enchufe, piso, lavaplatos, retrato, buzón, abrelatas, espejo	review of functions in Unidad 4 through Unidad 6	reading, writing	matching-completion, sentence completion	10

Section 1 (continued)

Test	Words Tested	Functions	Skills	Item Types	Points
Mid-Year	techo, despacho, espejo, televisor, sillón, enchufe, ondulado, licuadora, gorra, dedos, simpático, pijama, cuerpo, oreja, bata	review of functions in Unidad 1 through Unidad 6	reading, writing	matching, matching-completion, sentence completion	15
Unidad 7	barrer, limpiar, planchar, quitar, secar, trapo, plancha, secadora, trapeador, escoba, limpia, basura, sucia, polvo, limpio	identifying and naming household chores and housecleaning tools	reading, writing	matching-completion, matching/ sequencing	15
Unidad 8	el azúcar, la crema, la pimienta, la sal, las servilletas, los vasos, los platos, las tazas, las cerezas, la piña, las manzanas, los plátanos, la sandía, las uvas, las peras, la naranja	identifying and naming fruits and items used in table-setting, describing the location of objects	reading, writing	matching-completion, sentence completion	15
Unidad 9	avena, cereal, chocolate, huevos fritos, jugo, leche, mermelada, pan tostado, té, toronja, desayuno, huevos pasados por agua, huevos revueltos, margarina, beber	identifying and naming breakfast foods	reading, writing	matching-completion, sentence completion	15
Repaso: Unidades 7–9	sacar, secar, servilleta, té, tenedor, plancha, uvas, cerezas, huevos revueltos, cereal	review of functions in Unidad 7 through Unidad 9	reading writing	matching-completion, sentence completion	10

Section 1 (continued)

Test	Words Tested	Functions	Skills	Item Types	Points
Unidad 10	hamburguesa, legumbres, papas, pollo, queso, el arroz, la carne, los guisantes, el maís, el pavo, el pescado, las zanahorias, almorzar, gustar, poder, probar	identifying and naming lunch and supper foods	reading writing	matching-completion	15
Unidad 11	acostarse, bañarse, cepillarse, irse, lavarse, levantarse, peinarse, ponerse, quitarse, secarse, volver	identifying and naming routine daily activities	reading writing	matching-completion, sentence rewrite	15
Unidad 12	directora, enfermera, bibliotecario, maestra, conserje, biblioteca, enfermería, oficina, pasillo, salón de clase, bibliotecaria, cocinero, fuente de agua, subir, auditorio, entrada, bajar	identifying and relating the names of school locations and the people who work in them	reading writing	matching-completion, matching, labeling, sentence completion	15
End-of-Year	buzón, lámpara, cuchillo, batidora eléctrica, abrelatas, huevos, pan, regar, pone, toronja, nada, pequeña, baja, vestido, ceja	review of functions in Unidad 1 through Unidad 12	reading writing	matching, matching-completion, sentence completion	15

Section 2

Test	Structures Tested	Functions	Skills	Item Types	Points
Placement	structures in Unidad 1 through Unidad 12	functions in Unidad 1 through Unidad 12	reading, writing	matching-completion, sentence completion	20
Unidad 1	*duele, duelen;* definite article with parts of the body	telling about pain or discomfort; naming parts of the body	reading, writing	multiple-choice, sentence completion, matching	20 ★ 5
Unidad 2	*queda, quedan;* agreement of predicate adjectives; *de* indicating possession	describing articles of clothing; expressing ownership	reading, writing	sentence completion, multiple-choice	20 ★ 5
Unidad 3	present tense forms of *ser; más / menos… que*	describing people	reading, writing	sentence completion	20 ★ 5
Repaso: Unidades 1–3	review of structures in Unidad 1 through Unidad 3	review of functions in Unidad 1 through Unidad 3	reading, writing	matching-completion, sentence completion	15
Unidad 4	subject pronouns; present tense of *estar;* prepositions *dentro de, fuera de*	telling where people, places, and things are located	reading, writing	multiple-choice, labeling, chart completion, sentence completion	20 ★ 5

★ = extra credit

Section 2 (continued)

Test	Structures Tested	Functions	Skills	Item Types	Points
Unidad 5	nouns, singular/plural, masculine/feminine; adjectives, gender/number agreement; prepositions *delante de, detrás de, cerca de, lejos de*	describing locations; describing people and things	reading, writing	matching-completion, sentence completion, rewriting sentences	20 ★ 5
Unidad 6	present tense of regular *-ar, -er,* and *-ir* verbs	describing people's activities	reading, writing	sentence completion, paragraph completion	20 ★ 5
Repaso: Unidades 4–6	review of structures in Unidad 4 through Unidad 6	review of functions in Unidad 4 through Unidad 6	reading, writing	matching-completion, sentence completion	15
Mid-Year	review of structures in Unidad 1 through Unidad 6	review of functions in Unidad 1 through Unidad 6	reading, writing	sentence completion, sentence rewrite	20
Unidad 7	present tense of *tener (que)* and *acabar (de);* preposition *con*	telling what people have just done and have to do	reading, writing	matching-completion, paragraph completion	20 ★ 5
Unidad 8	present tense of *poner* and *traer*	telling about actions; describing the location of objects	reading, writing	multiple-choice, matching-completion, paragraph completion	20 ★ 5

Test	Structures Tested	Functions	Skills	Item Types	Points
Unidad 9	present tense of *querer*; possessive adjectives: *nuevo / viejo* adjective/noun agreement	expressing wants; telling about possessions	reading, writing	multiple-choice, sentence completion	20 ★ 5
Repaso: Unidades 7–9	review of structures in Unidad 7 through Unidad 9	review of functions in Unidad 7 through Unidad 9	reading, writing	sentence completion	15
Unidad 10	present tense of *o* to *ue* stem-changing verbs; *gusta / gustan;* indirect object pronouns; emphatic *a mí, a ti,* etc.	discussing lunch; describing likes and dislikes	reading, writing	matching-completion, sentence completion	20 ★ 5
Unidad 11	present tense of *e* to *ie* stem-changing verbs; regular, irregular, and stem-changing reflexive verbs; reflexive pronouns	describing daily activities	reading, writing	multiple-choice, matching-completion, paragraph completion	20 ★ 5
Unidad 12	present tense of *saber; saber* followed by an infinitive; superlative adjectives with *más* and *menos;* contrasting pairs *algo-nada, alguien-nadie,* etc.	telling about skills and abilities; comparing things	reading, writing	matching-completion, true or false, sentence completion	20 ★ 5
End-of-Year	review of structures in Unidad 1 through Unidad 12	review of functions in Unidad 1 through Unidad 12	reading, writing	matching-completion, true or false, sentence completion	20 ★ 5

Section 3

Test	Skills	Conversation Source	Auditory Item Types	Sounds Tested**	Points
Placement	listening, writing, speaking	new*	multiple-choice, dictation (word, sentence), question and answer	sounds presented in Unidad 1 through Unidad 12	25 (10 optional)
Unidad 1	listening, writing	Resource and Activity Book Master 150	true or false, dictation (word, sentence)	*n, ñ*	15 ★ 5 (10 optional)
Unidad 2	listening, writing	Resource and Activity Book Master 151	multiple-choice, dictation (word, sentence)	*h, j*	15 ★ 5 (10 optional)
Unidad 3	listening, writing	Resource and Activity Book Master 152	true or false, dictation (word, sentence)	*b, v*	15 ★ 5 (10 optional)
Repaso: Unidades 1–3	listening, writing	new	multiple-choice, dictation (word, sentence)	review of sounds in Unidad 1 through Unidad 3	15 (10 optional)
Unidad 4	listening, writing	Resource and Activity Book Master 153	true or false, dictation (word, sentence)	*a, e, i, o, u*	15 ★ 5 (10 optional)
Unidad 5	listening, writing	Resource and Activity Book Master 154	multiple-choice, dictation (word, sentence)	*r (ere)*	15 ★ 5 (10 optional)

*   For the text of new conversations, see pages T-24–T-60, "Oral Test Tapescript and Guide."
** Listening discrimination test parts appearing at the end of Section 3 are optional.
★ = extra credit

Section 3 (continued)

Test	Skills	Conversation Source	Auditory Item Types	Sounds Tested	Points
Unidad 6	listening, writing	Resource and Activity Book Master 155	true or false, dictation (word, sentence)	*r (erre)*	15 ★ 5 (10 optional)
Repaso: Unidades 4–6	listening, writing	new	multiple-choice, dictation (word, sentence)	review of sounds in Unidad 4 through Unidad 6	15 (10 optional)
Mid-Year	listening, writing	new	multiple-choice, dictation (word, sentence)	review of sounds in Unidad 1 through Unidad 6	15 (10 optional)
Unidad 7	listening, writing	Resource and Activity Book Master 156	multiple-choice, dictation (word, sentence)	*r (ere, erre)*	15 ★ 5 (10 optional)
Unidad 8	listening, writing	Resource and Activity Book Master 157	multiple-choice, dictation (word, sentence)	*s, z*	15 ★ 5 (10 optional)
Unidad 9	listening, writing	Resource and Activity Book Master 158	true or false, dictation (word, sentence)	*c (ce, ci)*	15 ★ 5 (10 optional)
Repaso: Unidades 7–9	listening, writing	new	multiple-choice, dictation (word, sentence)	review of sounds in Unidad 7 through Unidad 9	15 (10 optional)

Section 3 *(continued)*

Test	Skills	Conversation Source	Auditory Item Types	Sounds Tested	Points
Unidad 10	listening, writing	Resource and Activity Book Master 159	true or false, dictation (word, sentence)	*c (ca, co, cu)*	15 ★ 5 (10 optional)
Unidad 11	listening, writing	Resource and Activity Book Master 160	multiple-choice, dictation (word, sentence)	*q*	15 ★ 5 (10 optional)
Unidad 12	listening, writing	Resource and Activity Book Master 161	true or false, dictation (word, sentence)	*g (ga, go, gu)*	15 ★ 5 (10 optional)
End-of-Year	listening, writing	new	multiple-choice, dictation (word, sentence)	review of sounds in Unidad 1 through Unidad 12	15 (10 optional)

ORAL TEST TAPESCRIPT & GUIDE

In this section you will find the scripts for the oral sections of all the tests in the testing program. The scripts will help you preview the parts that are recorded on the audio Test Cassette and prepare for the teacher-administered parts of the oral sections. The following symbol indicates that the material has been recorded on the Test Cassette:

Conducting the Oral Section (Section 3)

The objective of a listening-comprehension assessment tool is to measure understanding of the language as it is spoken at a normal, natural pace by native speakers. It is recommended that you monitor your students as they listen to the Test Cassette and, if necessary, pause the tape to allow more time to write or rewind the tape and play a part again (for example, the conversation in Part A of Section 3).

Most of the material in Section 3 of each test should be familiar to students if you have presented each section of the regular units in the textbook. Therefore, your decision to pause or replay a specific part should be based on your students' abilities, their familiarity with the unit sections, and their exposure to the language and grammar of a unit as spoken by native speakers (i.e., the sections recorded on the Lesson and Exercise cassettes).

When you present the teacher-administered part of Section 3, it is recommended that you speak clearly, pleasantly, and at a natural, comfortable pace. You may wish to conduct practice dictations prior to the testing situation to determine an appropriate pace: a pace that is too slow may result in students becoming bored and easily distracted; a pace that is too fast may result in frustration and a negative attitude toward the testing experience. Because the tests are power tests and not speed tests, the objective is to obtain an accurate measure of students' ability to comprehend the spoken language while maintaining their enthusiasm for learning Spanish as a second language.

A. Listen to the conversation between Pablo and his father. Then you will hear five multiple-choice statements about their conversation. Circle the letter of the phrase that best completes each statement.

PAPA:	Pablo, ¿qué pasa?
PABLO:	¡Hola, papá! ¡Qué problema! Todos mis amigos quieren hablar de cosas diferentes.
PAPÁ:	¿Cómo?
PABLO:	Roberto sólo quiere hablar de su desayuno, los huevos fritos, el pan, la mermelada de fresa…
PAPÁ:	No comprendo el problema.
PABLO:	Cecilia sólo quiere hablar de matemáticas…
PAPÁ:	Bueno, está bien.
PABLO:	Papá, Rosa todo el tiempo quiere hablar de las legumbres y de las frutas como la sandía, la piña, los plátanos, las cerezas…
PAPÁ:	Bueno, a ella le gustan mucho las frutas.
PABLO:	David sólo quiere hablar de su casa. Los muebles, los cuartos, la cocina, el garaje…
PAPÁ:	Bueno, Pablo, no comprendo el problema.
PABLO:	Papá, yo quiero hablar de trabajos diferentes. No sé si quiero ser cocinero, secretario o director. No sé si quiero ser bibliotecario o enfermero. No sé…
PAPÁ:	Adiós, Pablo. Yo también tengo un problema.

1. Pablo tiene…
   a. una hermana.
   b. un problema.
   c. una piña.

2. Roberto sólo quiere hablar de…
   a. matemáticas.
   b. carros.
   c. su desayuno.

3. Cecilia sólo quiere hablar de…
   a. frutas.
   b. autobuses y trenes.
   c. matemáticas.

4. David sólo quiere hablar de…
   a. su casa.
   b. legumbres.
   c. Europa.

5. El papá de Pablo…
   a. comprende el problema de Pablo.
   b. dice "adiós."
   c. habla de matemáticas.

---

*Notes regarding the tests are presented in this section in brackets and italic letters. They are not recorded on the Test Cassette.

Placement Test, *continued*

 B. Dictado. Listen carefully to these sentences. You will hear each sentence twice. Write the missing words on the answer blanks.

[Each sentence is given twice on the Test Cassette. There is a three-second pause on the tape for students to write answers. You may wish to pause the tape manually to allow more time for students to write.]

1. Mi tía es dueña de una compañía.
2. Hoy almorzamos con ella.
3. Vive lejos de aquí.
4. Cocina muy bien.
5. Siempre sirve algo bueno.

C. Speaking

[The Speaking Section of the Placement Test contains ten questions that count one point each. Credit should be given for the accuracy, completeness, and appropriateness of each answer. Students should be encouraged to answer each question as completely as they can but should not be penalized for failure to use complete sentences. Although natural, conversational responses are the goal, a phrase or one-word response should be given full credit if it is correct.

Materials needed: outline drawings of school locations (see Resource and Activity Book); a blank sheet of paper and a pencil.]

1. ¿Cómo estás?
2. ¿Vives en una casa o en un apartamento?
3. ¿Qué haces en la casa? (¿Cómo limpias la casa?)
4. ¿Qué te gusta comer para el desayuno? (...para la cena?)
5. ¿A qué hora te despiertas?
6. ¿Qué deporte practicas?
7. ¿Dónde están muchas sillas—en el pasillo o en el auditorio? *[Hold up outline drawings of school locations.]*
8. ¿Conoces a un enfermero o a una enfermera?
9. Muéstrame tu boca. Muéstrame tu frente.
10. Por favor, escribe la palabra **español** en el papel.

D. Listen carefully to these twelve words. You will hear each word twice. Complete each word by writing a vowel or consonant letter on the answer blank. The first two have been done for you. (This test part is optional. Point values should not be applied to students' scores.)

1. mesa, mesa
2. sal, sal
3. jueves, jueves
4. hija, hija
5. llevar, llevar
6. pollo, pollo
7. noche, noche
8. queso, queso
9. sucia, sucia
10. rubio, rubio
11. cerca, cerca
12. guerra, guerra

A. Listen to the conversation between Víctor and his **mamá**. Then you will hear five multiple-choice statements about their conversation. You will hear each statement twice. Circle the letter of the phrase that best completes each statement.

MAMÁ: Víctor, son las siete y media de la mañana. Ya es hora de ir a la escuela.

VÍCTOR: ¡Estoy muy mal! ¡Ayyy! Tengo mucho dolor.

MAMÁ: ¿Qué te duele, hijo?

VÍCTOR: Ay, mamá, me duelen la cabeza, las piernas y los brazos.

MAMÁ: ¿Te duele todo el cuerpo?

VÍCTOR: Sí, me duele todo el cuerpo. Me duelen los ojos, las manos, los dientes, las...

MAMÁ: ¡Víctor! No te duele todo el cuerpo. Hoy vas a la escuela.

VÍCTOR: ¡Por favor, mamá! Tengo un examen de historia hoy. ¡Hasta me duelen las pestañas!

MAMÁ: ¡Qué muchacho! ¡A la escuela! ¡Ahora mismo!

[Each multiple-choice statement is given twice on the Test Cassette.]

1. Son las siete y media...
 a. de la noche.
 b. de la mañana.
 c. de la tarde.

2. Víctor tiene...
 a. mucha prisa.
 b. sueño.
 c. un examen.

3. Es un examen de...
 a. historia.
 b. ciencias.
 c. matemáticas.

4. Víctor va...
 a. a la casa.
 b. al cine.
 c. a la escuela.

5. Víctor va...
 a. mañana.
 b. ahora mismo.
 c. a las nueve.

B. Dictado. Listen, and then write the missing words. You will hear each sentence twice.

[Each sentence is given twice on the Test Cassette.]

PAPÁ: ¿Qué te duele, Carlitos?

CARLITOS: Me duele la cabeza.

PAPÁ: ¿Cuánto y cuándo te duele?

CARLITOS: Me duele mucho los viernes a las siete de la mañana porque tengo clase de ciencias.

C. Now try writing these sentences for extra credit. You will hear each sentence twice.

[Read each of the following sentences twice.]

1. No estoy bien de salud.
2. Tengo los ojos rojos.
3. Tengo dolor de cabeza.
4. Me duele el cuerpo.
5. Tienes la gripe.

D. Listen carefully to these twelve words. You will hear each word twice. Complete each word by writing **n** or **ñ** on the answer blank. The first two have been done for you. (This test part is optional. Point values should not be applied to students' scores.)

1. bueno, bueno
2. año, año
3. punto, punto
4. sueño, sueño

5. niño, niño
6. mano, mano
7. nietos, nietos
8. español, español

9. inglés, inglés
10. cintura, cintura
11. doña, doña
12. junio, junio

A. Listen to the conversation between señora Oteo and a salesclerk. Then you will hear five statements about their conversation. You will hear each statement twice. Circle **CIERTO** if the statement is true. Circle **FALSO** if it is false.

SRA. OTEO:	Buenas tardes, señorita. ¿Tiene usted una blusa y una falda?
VENDEDORA:	En esta tienda hay blusas, faldas, chaquetas y pantalones. También hay zapatos muy bonitos.
SRA. OTEO:	¿Hay ropa pequeña?
VENDEDORA:	Hay ropa pequeña, mediana y grande.
SRA. OTEO:	Esta blusa pequeña es muy bonita.
VENDEDORA:	Sí, señora. Pero a usted le va a quedar bien una blusa grande.
SRA. OTEO:	No, no, no. Voy a comprar la blusa pequeña. También voy a comprar una falda mediana.
VENDEDORA:	Una falda mediana le va a quedar muy mal, señora. Aquí está una falda grande.
SRA. OTEO:	¡Señorita! La falda no es para mí. Mi prima va a llevar la falda. ¡Y mi hija va a llevar la blusa!
VENDEDORA:	¡Ay, perdón, señora!

¿Cierto o falso?

[Each statement is given twice on the Test Cassette.]

1. La señora Oteo va a comprar una chaqueta.
2. En la tienda hay pantalones y zapatos.
3. La blusa pequeña es fea.
4. La prima de la señora Oteo va a llevar la falda.
5. La hija de la señora Oteo va a llevar la blusa.

B. Dictado. Listen and write the missing words. You will hear each sentence twice.

[Each sentence is given twice on the Test Cassette.]

RAÚL:	¿Dónde está mi ropa de verano?
MAMÁ:	No tienes.
RAÚL:	¿De quién es la chaqueta? Es bonita.
MAMÁ:	Es de tu hermano Carlos. Te queda pequeña.
RAÚL:	¿De quién es el sombrero?
MAMÁ:	Es de tu primo Pedro.
RAÚL:	¿Y los zapatos? ¡Son feos!
MAMÁ:	Son tus zapatos nuevos para ir a la escuela.

C. Now try writing these sentences for extra credit. You will hear each sentence twice.

[Read each of the following sentences twice.]

1. Paula tiene ojos bonitos.
2. Tiene el pelo negro.
3. Su vestido es fantástico.
4. Tiene una carita muy bonita.
5. Paula es una niña de doce días.

D. Listen carefully to the following words. You will hear each word twice. If a word has an **h** in it, circle **sí**. If it does not, circle **no**. The first two have been done for you. (This test part is optional. Point values should not be applied to students' scores.)

1. hija, hija
2. oreja, oreja
3. ahora, ahora
4. loro, loro

5. ojo, ojo
6. historia, historia
7. hermano, hermano
8. hace, hace

9. ceja, ceja
10. hay, hay
11. hermana, hermana
12. cara, cara

A. Listen to the conversation between Estela and Alicia. Then you will hear five multiple-choice statements about their conversation. You will hear each statement twice. Circle the letter of the word that best completes each statement.

ESTELA:	¡Qué fotografías tan bonitas! ¿De quiénes son las fotos, Alicia?
ALICIA:	Son de mis amigos, Estela. Este muchacho es Enrique. Él tiene el pelo rojizo y los ojos castaños.
ESTELA:	¿Y este muchacho tan alto?
ALICIA:	Es Manuel. Es más alto y más delgado que Enrique. Tiene el pelo rubio, corto y muy rizado.
ESTELA:	Y la muchacha, ¿es baja?
ALICIA:	¿Gertrudis? No, ella es alta y gruesa.
ESTELA:	Y esta foto es de…
ALICIA:	¡Soy yo! Soy muy bonita, inteligente, simpática, generosa…
ESTELA:	¡Y muy modesta!

[Each multiple-choice statement is given twice on the Test Cassette.]

1. Los ojos de Enrique son…
   a. azules.
   b. castaños.
   c. bonitos.

2. Enrique tiene el pelo…
   a. rojizo.
   b. castaño.
   c. alto.

3. Manuel es…
   a. bajo.
   b. modesto.
   c. delgado.

4. Gertrudis es…
   a. baja.
   b. alta.
   c. generosa.

5. Gertrudis también es…
   a. bonita.
   b. tímida.
   c. gruesa.

B. Dictado. Listen carefully and write the missing words. You will hear each sentence twice.

[Each sentence is given twice on the Test Cassette.]

1. ¿De qué color son tus ojos?
2. Tengo los ojos castaños.
3. ¿Cómo son los ojos de tu mamá?
4. Son más grandes que mis ojos.
5. Ella tiene los ojos verdes.

Unidad 3: Unit Test, continued

C. Now try writing these sentences for extra credit. You will hear each sentence twice.

[Read each of the following sentences twice.]

1. Yo soy más alta que Ana.
2. Ana es menos alta que María.
3. María es menos alta que yo.
4. Sara es más alta que yo.
5. ¿Es Ana más alta que Sara?

D. Listen carefully to the following words. You will hear each word twice. Complete each word by writing **b** or **v** on the answer blank. The first four have been done for you. (This test part is optional. Point values should not be applied to students' scores.)

1. bajo, bajo
2. abajo, abajo
3. verano, verano
4. primavera, primavera
5. verdad, verdad
6. abrigo, abrigo
7. blusa, blusa
8. noviembre, noviembre
9. abuela, abuela
10. vas, vas
11. cabeza, cabeza
12. botas, botas
13. divertido, divertido
14. veinte, veinte

REPASO: UNIDADES 1–3 ACHIEVEMENT REVIEW TEST

[Test masters 35–36]

 A. Listen to the conversation between Liliana and Rosa. Then you will hear five statements about their conversation. You will hear each statement twice. Circle **CIERTO** if the statement is true. Circle **FALSO** if it is false.

LILIANA:	Rosa, ¿por qué no compras este suéter verde?
ROSA:	No me gusta. El color no va bien con mis ojos azules.
LILIANA:	Bueno. ¿Por qué no compras este azul entonces?
ROSA:	No, gracias. El azul no va bien con mi pelo rojizo. No voy a comprar un suéter.
LILIANA:	¿Qué vas a comprar entonces? ¿Una blusa? Mira qué bonita esta blusa blanca.
ROSA:	No, gracias. No me gustan las blusas.
LILIANA:	¿No te gustan las blusas? ¿Por qué?
ROSA:	Las blusas no me quedan bien.
LILIANA:	¡Ay Rosa, qué difícil eres!

¿Cierto o falso?

[Each statement is given twice on the Test Cassette.]

1. Rosa tiene ojos azules.
2. Rosa tiene el pelo castaño.
3. A Rosa le gusta el suéter azul.
4. A Rosa no le gustan las blusas.
5. A Rosa las blusas le quedan bien.

 B. Dictado. Listen carefully to these sentences. You will hear each sentence twice. Write the missing words on the answer blanks.

[Each sentence is given twice on the Test Cassette. You may wish to pause the tape manually after each sentence has been repeated.]

1. ¿Cómo es tu hermana?
2. Mi hermana es generosa.
3. Ella tiene el pelo rubio.
4. Sus ojos son bonitos.
5. Yo soy más baja que ella.

C. Listen carefully to these twelve words. You will hear each word twice. Complete each word by writing a vowel or a consonant on the answer blank. The first two have been done for you.

1. una, una
2. humano, humano
3. español, español
4. hijo, hijo

5. baño, baño
6. ventana, ventana
7. historia, historia
8. año, año

9. negro, negro
10. doña, doña
11. boca, boca
12. vestido, vestido

UNIDAD 4: UNIT TEST [Test masters 43–44]

A. Listen to this conversation between Pacha and Celia. Then you will hear five statements about their conversation. You will hear each statement twice. Circle **CIERTO** if the statement is true. Circle **FALSO** if it is false.

PACHA: ¡Hola! ¡Celia! ¿Dónde estás? ¿Estás en casa?

CELIA: Estoy en la sala. Entra, Pacha.

PACHA: Bueno, yo también estoy en la sala. ¿Dónde estás tú?

CELIA: ¡Uf! ¡No, no, no!...Estoy en la cocina.

PACHA: Pues, yo estoy en la cocina. ¿Dónde estás?

CELIA: ¡Puf! ¡Ay! ¡Uf!...Estoy fuera de la casa. Estoy en el patio...en el jardín.

PACHA: ¡Mira, chica! Estoy en el patio y ahora en el jardín. ¡Tú no estás aquí! ¿Dónde estás?

CELIA: Estoy dentro del garaje. ¡Ayyy!

PACHA: ¡Por fin! Ahora estamos en el mismo lugar. ¿Qué pasa?

CELIA: Es que...es que el perrito tiene mi libro para la clase de español. ¡Y él va más rápido que yo!

¿Cierto o falso?

[Each statement is given twice on the Test Cassette.]

1. Pacha está en la casa de Celia.
2. Pacha está con Celia en la cocina.
3. Celia y el perrito están en el garaje.
4. Pacha tiene el libro de español.
5. El perrito tiene el libro de español.

B. Dictado. Listen carefully to these sentences. You will hear each sentence twice. Write the missing words on the answer blanks.

[Each sentence is given twice on the Test Cassette. You may wish to pause the tape manually after each sentence has been repeated.]

1. ¿Cómo es tu casa?
2. Es muy grande.
3. Tiene seis dormitorios.
4. ¿Hay garaje?
5. Sí. Tiene patio también.

Unidad 4: Unit Test, continued

C. Now try writing these sentences for extra credit. You will hear each sentence twice.

[Read each of the following sentences twice in a loud, clear, pleasant voice.]

1. ¿Dónde está Elena?
2. Está dentro de la casa.
3. ¿En qué cuarto está?
4. Está en su dormitorio.
5. Siempre estudia en su cuarto.

D. Listen carefully to these twelve words. You will hear each word twice. Complete each word by writing **a, e, i, o**, or **u** on the answer blank. The first two have been done for you. (This test part is optional. Point values should not be applied to students' scores.)

1. patio, patio
2. buzón, buzón
3. sótano, sótano
4. cocina, cocina

5. dormitorio, dormitorio
6. dentro, dentro
7. ustedes, ustedes
8. balcones, balcones

9. despacho, despacho
10. una, una
11. garaje, garaje
12. chimenea, chimenea

A. Listen to the conversation between Esteban, Sr. Olvida, and Raquel. Then you will hear five multiple-choice statements about their conversation. You will hear each statement twice. Circle the letter of the phrase that best completes each statement.

ESTEBAN:	Señor Olvida, ¿dónde va el televisor? ¿Delante del sofá?
SR. OLVIDA:	A ver, Esteban, a ver…no, por favor, en…
RAQUEL:	¿Aquí, en la alfombra?
SR. OLVIDA:	No, Raquel, no…cerca de…
ESTEBAN:	¿Va cerca del estante?
SR. OLVIDA:	No, no…detrás de…
RAQUEL:	¿Va detrás de la lámpara?
SR. OLVIDA:	No. No va detrás de la lámpara.
ESTEBAN:	¡Uf! Va aquí en el piso. Adiós, señor Olvida.
RAQUEL:	¡Ay! ¡Qué dolor tengo en los brazos! Adiós.

[Each multiple-choice statement is given twice on the Test Cassette.]

1. Esteban tiene…
   a. un sofá.
   b. un televisor.
   c. una alfombra.

2. El señor Olvida habla con…
   a. un muchacho.
   b. una muchacha.
   c. un muchacho y una muchacha.

3. El televisor va…
   a. cerca del estante.
   b. detrás de la lámpara.
   c. en el piso.

4. A Raquel le duelen…
   a. las manos.
   b. los brazos.
   c. los pies.

5. Raquel y Esteban dicen "adiós"…
   a. al muchacho.
   b. al señor Olvida.
   c. a la muchacha.

B. Dictado. Listen carefully to these sentences. You will hear each sentence twice. Write the missing words on the answer blanks.

[Each sentence is given twice on the Test Cassette. You may wish to pause the tape manually after each sentence has been repeated.]

1. ¿Cómo es la sala?
2. Es grande y tiene muchos muebles.
3. ¿Cuántos sillones hay?

4. Hay un sillón y un sofá.

5. ¿El piso tiene alfombra?

C. Now try writing these sentences for extra credit. You will hear each sentence twice.

[Read each of the following sentences twice.]

1. ¿Dónde está el televisor?

2. Está en la sala.

3. ¿Tiene usted radio?

4. Sí, está en el estante.

5. ¿Hay teléfono aquí?

D. You will hear a number and a word. If the word has an **r** sound, circle the number. If the word does not have an **r** sound, do not circle the number. The first two have been done for you. (This test part is optional. Point values should not be applied to students' scores.)

1. cortina	**5.** delante	**9.** Mario
2. alta	**6.** detrás	**10.** tímido
3. caro	**7.** anda	**11.** bonito
4. lámpara	**8.** tengo	**12.** madre

A. Listen to the conversation between Iris and her father. Then you will hear five statements about their conversation. You will hear each statement twice. Circle **CIERTO** if the statement is true. Circle **FALSO** if it is false.

Papá:	¡Hoy vamos a cocinar!
Iris:	¡Qué bien! ¿Cómo voy a ayudar, papá?
Papá:	Primero, tú vas a abrir esta lata. Yo voy a usar la batidora eléctrica.
Iris:	De acuerdo. ¿Dónde está el abrelatas?
Papá:	Está dentro del gabinete cerca del refrigerador.
Iris:	No, papá. El abrelatas no está aquí.
Papá:	Entonces, está en el cajón.
Iris:	No está aquí tampoco, papá. Papá, el abrelatas no está en la cocina.
Papá:	¡Ay, tienes razón Iris! Vamos al restaurante.

¿Cierto o falso?

[Each statement is given twice on the Test Cassette.]

1. Iris y su papá están en la cocina.
2. Iris va a abrir una caja.
3. Papá va a usar el grifo.
4. Cerca del refrigerador hay un gabinete.
5. El abrelatas no está en la cocina.

B. Dictado. Listen carefully to these sentences. You will hear each sentence twice. Write the missing words on the answer blanks.

[Each sentence is given twice on the Test Cassette. You may wish to pause the tape manually after each sentence has been repeated.]

1. En tu casa, ¿todos cocinan?
2. No, yo no cocino.
3. ¿Usan el horno de microondas?
4. Sí, y usamos el lavaplatos.
5. ¿Hay batidora eléctrica?

C. Now try writing these sentences for extra credit. You will hear each sentence twice.

[Read each of the following sentences twice.]

1. ¿Qué te gusta hacer?
2. Me gusta leer.
3. ¿Estudias ahora?
4. Mi hermano y yo estudiamos.
5. ¿Abro el libro?

D. Listen carefully to these twelve words. You will hear each word twice. If you hear the consonant sound **erre** in a word, circle **sí**. If you do not hear the consonant sound **erre**, circle **no**. The first two have been done for you. (This test part is optional. Point values should not be applied to students' scores.)

1. corre, corre	5. arroz, arroz	9. ¿cuántos?, ¿cuántos?
2. luego, luego	6. borrador, borrador	10. paredes, paredes
3. rica, rica	7. estufa, estufa	11. ropero, ropero
4. ustedes, ustedes	8. carro, carro	12. baila, baila

REPASO: UNIDADES 4–6 ACHIEVEMENT REVIEW TEST

[Test masters 69–70]

A. Listen to the conversation between Alma and Pedro. Then you will hear five multiple-choice statements about their conversation. Circle the letter of the phrase that best completes each statement.

ALMA: ¡Pedro! ¿Dónde estás?

PEDRO: Estoy en la sala con Felipe. ¿Dónde estás tú?

ALMA: Estoy en el patio. La puerta de tu casa no abre.

PEDRO: Sí. Mi tío Javier pinta la puerta. Yo abro la ventana.

ALMA: Gracias, Pedro. Ahora, ¿dónde están Felipe y tú? ¡No hay luz!

PEDRO: Estamos cerca de la lámpara. Mi tío pinta la bombilla. Abro las cortinas.

ALMA: ¡Caramba! ¿Qué es esto, Pedro?

PEDRO: Es el espejo.

ALMA: ¡Es anaranjado!

PEDRO: Sí. A mi tío le gusta mucho pintar. Pinta el espejo también.

1. Pedro y Felipe están…
   a. en la cocina.
   b. en la sala.
   c. en el dormitorio.

2. Alma está en…
   a. el patio.
   b. la sala.
   c. el comedor.

3. El tío de Pedro se llama…
   a. Alma.
   b. Felipe.
   c. Javier.

4. Al tío de Pedro le gusta mucho…
   a. comer.
   b. hablar.
   c. pintar.

5. Pedro abre…
   a. las cortinas.
   b. la puerta.
   c. el espejo.

B. Dictado. Listen carefully to these sentences. You will hear each sentence twice. Write the missing words on the answer blanks.

[Each sentence is given twice on the Test Cassette. You may wish to pause the tape manually after each sentence has been repeated.]

1. En el verano comemos en el patio.
2. El patio está detrás de la casa.
3. A mi mamá le gusta cocinar.
4. Mi hermana come mucho.
5. Mis hermanos cocinan bien.

Repaso: Unidades 4–6, continued

C. Listen carefully to these twelve words. You will hear each word twice. Complete each word by writing a vowel or consonant letter on the answer blank. The first two have been done for you. (This test part is optional. Point values should not be applied to students' scores.)

1. están, están
2. ropa, ropa
3. biblioteca, biblioteca
4. trabajo, trabajo

5. perro, perro
6. sucio, sucio
7. vida, vida
8. tomar, tomar

9. mujer, mujer
10. techo, techo
11. río, río
12. alfombra, alfombra

A. Listen to the conversation between Teresa and Manuel. Then you will hear five multiple-choice statements about their conversation. Circle the letter of the phrase that best completes each statement.

TERESA: ¡Hola, Manuel! ¿Cómo estás?

MANUEL: ¡Hola Teresa! Estoy así, así. Vivimos en una casa nueva.

TERESA: ¡Qué bueno! ¡Felicidades, Manuel!

MANUEL: Gracias. La casa tiene una cocina con horno de microondas, una estufa grande, un refrigerador y un abrelatas. También tiene un comedor grande.

TERESA: ¡Fantástico!

MANUEL: Sí. Y mi dormitorio tiene dos ventanas. Pero…

TERESA: ¿Pero qué? ¿Hay un problema?

MANUEL: Sí. La casa esta muy lejos de la escuela. Y yo camino a la escuela. ¡Me duelen los pies!

TERESA: ¡Ay, esto es un problema!

1. La familia de Manuel vive en…
   a. un apartamento.
   b. una casa.
   c. una escuela.

2. La cocina tiene…
   a. un refrigerador.
   b. una alfombra.
   c. un sofá.

3. El comedor es…
   a. pequeño.
   b. mediano.
   c. grande.

4. El dormitorio de Manuel tiene…
   a. dos puertas.
   b. dos ventanas.
   c. dos camas.

5. A Manuel le duelen…
   a. los ojos.
   b. los pies.
   c. los brazos.

B. Dictado. Listen carefully to these sentences. You will hear each sentence twice. Write the missing words on the answer blanks.

[Each sentence is given twice on the Test Cassette. You may wish to pause the tape manually after each sentence has been repeated.]

1. ¿Vives cerca de aquí?
2. No, mi casa está lejos.
3. ¿Cómo es el patio?
4. Es muy grande.
5. Está detrás de la casa.

Mid-Year Test, continued

C. Listen carefully to these twelve words. You will hear each word twice. Complete each word by writing a vowel or consonant letter on the answer blank. The first two have been done for you. (This test part is optional. Point values should not be applied to students' scores.)

1. casi, casi
2. enseña, enseña
3. hotel, hotel
4. mesa, mesa

5. vaca, vaca
6. loro, loro
7. lugar, lugar
8. nacho, nacho

9. hablar, hablar
10. piña, piña
11. cine, cine
12. también, también

UNIDAD 7: UNIT TEST [Test masters 85–86]

A. Listen to the conversation between a mother, father, son, and daughter. Then you will hear five statements about their conversation. You will hear each statement twice. Circle **CIERTO** if the statement is true. Circle **FALSO** if it is false.

MAMÁ: ¡Qué barbaridad! Tenemos que limpiar la casa.

PAPÁ: Yo tengo que lavar, secar y planchar la ropa.

HIJO: Yo acabo de limpiar el piso y pasar la aspiradora.

MAMÁ: Yo acabo de quitar el polvo. Tengo que sacar la basura. También tengo que regar las plantas.

PAPÁ: Y tú, hija, ¿qué tienes que hacer?

HIJA: Bueno, ¡yo tengo que inspeccionar la casa limpia!

¿Cierto o falso?

[Each statement is given twice on the Test Cassette.]

1. La mamá tiene que hacer todo.
2. El papá tiene que lavar la ropa.
3. El hijo acaba de limpiar el piso.
4. La mamá acaba de pasar la aspiradora.
5. La mamá tiene que regar las plantas.

B. Dictado. Listen carefully to these sentences. You will hear each sentence twice. Write the missing words on the answer blanks.

[Each sentence is given twice on the Test Cassette. You may wish to pause the tape manually after each sentence has been repeated.]

1. ¿Qué tienes que hacer en tu casa?
2. Yo tengo que barrer los pisos.
3. Mi mamá lava la ropa.
4. Mi hermano quita el polvo.
5. Mi papá seca la ropa.

C. Now try writing these sentences for extra credit. You will hear each sentence twice.

[Read each of the following sentences twice.]

1. Acabo de limpiar la cocina.
2. ¿Qué acaba de hacer Raúl?
3. Acaba de recoger la ropa.

    4. ¿Qué acaban de hacer ustedes?

    5. Acabamos de lavar los platos.

D. Listen carefully to these twelve words. You will hear each word twice. Complete each word by writing **r** or **rr** on the answer blank. The first two have been done for you. (This test part is optional. Point values should not be applied to students' scores.)

1. caro, caro	**5.** hablar, hablar	**9.** reloj, reloj
2. carro, carro	**6.** ropa, ropa	**10.** arriba, arriba
3. perro, perro	**7.** sacar, sacar	**11.** rápido, rápido
4. pero, pero	**8.** carta, carta	**12.** basura, basura

UNIDAD 8: UNIT TEST [Test masters 93–94]

A. Listen to the conversation between Cecilia and Juan. Then you will hear five multiple-choice statements about their conversation. You will hear each statement twice. Circle the letter of the phrase that best completes each statement.

CECILIA:	¡Hola, Juan! ¿Cómo estás?
JUAN:	Hola, Cecilia. Estoy así, así.
CECILIA:	¿Qué tienes? ¿Estás enfermo?
JUAN:	No. Tengo hambre.
CECILIA:	¡Caramba! Tienes suerte. Ahora yo voy a comer frutas. Vamos, Juan.
JUAN:	Sí, gracias. Me gustan las manzanas, las uvas, las fresas...
CECILIA:	A mí también me gustan mucho. ¡Ah! No tenemos manzanas, uvas o fresas.
JUAN:	También me gustan los plátanos, las cerezas y la piña.
CECILIA:	Lo siento, Juan. No tenemos piña. Vamos a la mesa para comer sandía.
JUAN:	¡Caramba! Ya no tengo hambre. No me gusta la sandía.

[Each multiple-choice statement is given twice on the Test Cassette.]

1. Juan está...
   a. muy bien.
   b. así, así.
   c. contento.

2. Cecilia va a...
   a. comer frutas.
   b. comprar ropa.
   c. estudiar inglés.

3. A Cecilia le gustan las manzanas, las uvas y las...
   a. peras.
   b. papas.
   c. fresas.

4. A Juan no le gusta...
   a. la sandía.
   b. la piña.
   c. comer manzanas.

5. Ahora, Juan no tiene...
   a. hambre.
   b. sed.
   c. frío.

B. Dictado. Listen carefully to these sentences. You will hear each sentence twice. Write the missing words on the answer blanks.

[Each sentence is given twice on the Test Cassette. You may wish to pause the tape manually after each sentence has been repeated.]

1. Vamos a poner la mesa.
2. Pepe pone el azúcar y la crema.

3. Amalia pone la sal y la pimienta.
4. Luisa pone las servilletas.
5. Yo pongo el mantel.

C. Now try writing these sentences for extra credit. You will hear each sentence twice.

[Read each of the following sentences twice.]

1. ¿Qué frutas traen ustedes?
2. Yo traigo naranjas.
3. Celia trae la sandía.
4. Ricardo trae manzanas.
5. Catalina trae uvas.

D. Listen carefully to these twelve words. You will hear each word twice. Complete each word by writing **s** or **z** on the answer blank. The first two have been done for you. (This test part is optional. Point values should not be applied to students' scores.)

1. música, música
2. zapato, zapato
3. pizarra, pizarra
4. gusto, gusto
5. hasta, hasta
6. marzo, marzo
7. escribe, escribe
8. agosto, agosto
9. azul, azul
10. cosa, cosa
11. buzón, buzón
12. zoológico, zoológico

A. Listen to the conversation between David and Hugo. Then you will hear five statements about their conversation. You will hear each statement twice. Circle **CIERTO** if the statement is true. Circle **FALSO** if it is false.

DAVID: Buenos días, Hugo. ¿Qué quieres tomar para el desayuno?

HUGO: Buenos días, David. ¿Qué vas a tomar tú?

DAVID: ¿Yo? Siempre tomo huevos fritos, pan tostado, cereal con leche y jugo de naranja. ¿Qué tomas en México por la mañana?

HUGO: A veces como tortillas con frijoles. Generalmente tomo un pan dulce y una taza de chocolate bien caliente.

DAVID: ¿Es todo?

HUGO: Sí, cómo no.

DAVID: ¡Caramba! Tu desayuno es como la dieta de mi mamá.

¿Cierto o falso?

[Each statement is given twice on the Test Cassette.]

1. Hugo y David hablan por la mañana.
2. David come poco en el desayuno.
3. Hugo no come por la mañana.
4. A veces Hugo come tortillas por la mañana.
5. A Hugo le gusta una taza de chocolate con su desayuno.

B. Dictado. Listen carefully to these sentences. You will hear each sentence twice. Write the missing words on the answer blanks.

[Each sentence is given twice on the Test Cassette. You may wish to pause the tape manually after each sentence has been repeated.]

1. ¿Qué quieres para el desayuno?
2. Yo quiero huevos pasados por agua.
3. Ramona quiere cereal.
4. ¿Qué jugo toman?
5. Tomamos jugo de naranja.

C. Now try writing these sentences for extra credit. You will hear each sentence twice.

[Read each of the following sentences twice.]

1. ¿Es nueva tu casa?
2. No, mi casa es vieja.
3. ¿Son nuevos tus muebles?
4. Los muebles son de mis papás.
5. ¿Son nuevos sus muebles?

D. You will hear a number and a word. If the word has the soft sound of the letter **c** in it, circle the number. If the word does not have the soft **c**, do not circle the number. The first three have been done for you. (This test part is optional. Point values should not be applied to students' scores.)

1. centro	**6.** quiero	**10.** trece
2. cinco	**7.** nunca	**11.** difícil
3. cuatro	**8.** veces	**12.** cine
4. tocino	**9.** cuarto	**13.** cereza
5. once		

A. Listen to the conversation between Rubén and Rita. Then you will hear five multiple-choice statements about their conversation. Circle the letter of the phrase that best completes each statement.

RUBÉN: ¡Buenos días, Rita! ¿Qué haces?

RITA: ¡Hola, Rubén! Acabo de poner la mesa. ¿Quieres tomar el desayuno?

RUBÉN: No, gracias. Acabo de comer huevos fritos, avena y un plátano.

RITA: Es un desayuno grande, ¿no?

RUBÉN: Sí, es. Hoy tengo que limpiar el garaje. ¿Qué traes a la mesa?

RITA: Es mermelada de fresas para el pan tostado. ¿Quieres pan?

RUBÉN: No, gracias. ¡Ah, toronjas!

RITA: Son muy deliciosas. ¿Quieres una?

RUBÉN: No, gracias. Tengo que limpiar el garaje ahora mismo.

RITA: Es cierto. El garaje está muy sucio.

RUBÉN: Rita, tienes que poner un plato más.

RITA: ¿Por qué?

RUBÉN: Porque ahora sí tengo hambre.

1. Rita acaba de…
   a. comprar huevos.
   b. desayunar.
   c. poner la mesa.

2. Rubén acaba de…
   a. comer.
   b. planchar.
   c. lavar la ropa.

3. Rubén tiene que limpiar…
   a. el garaje.
   b. el piso.
   c. la casa.

4. Para el desayuno, Rita trae…
   a. fresas.
   b. toronjas.
   c. plátanos.

5. Rita tiene que poner un plato más porque Rubén tiene…
   a. sed.
   b. hambre.
   c. frío.

B. Dictado. Listen carefully to these sentences. You will hear each sentence twice. Write the missing words on the answer blanks.

[Each sentence is given twice on the Test Cassette. You may wish to pause the tape manually after each sentence has been repeated.]

1. ¿Dónde está mi perrito?
2. Está debajo de la mesa.
3. Tu perrito tiene que comer.
4. El perrito no quiere nada.
5. Él acaba de comer mucho.

C. Listen carefully to these twelve words. You will hear each word twice. Complete each word by writing the missing letter on the answer blank. The first two have been done for you. (This test part is optional. Point values should not be applied to students' scores.)

1. pera, pera
2. sofá, sofá
3. perro, perro
4. zapato, zapato
5. cerca, cerca
6. radio, radio
7. taza, taza
8. cereal, cereal
9. pasados, pasados
10. porque, porque
11. veces, veces
12. corre, corre

UNIDAD 10: UNIT TEST [Test masters 117–118]

A. Listen to the conversation between Mirta and Eduardo. Then you will hear five multiple-choice statements about their conversation. You will hear each statement twice. Circle the letter of the phrase that best completes each statement.

EDUARDO: ¡Hola, Mirta! ¿Vas a casa?

MIRTA: Sí, voy a almorzar.

EDUARDO: Yo también. Tengo hambre.

MIRTA: ¿Adónde vas?

EDUARDO: Voy a la casa de Alberto. Almuerzo con él.

MIRTA: Y, ¿qué va a comer Alberto?

EDUARDO: ¡Uf! A él sólo le gustan las legumbres.

MIRTA: ¿Qué te gusta comer para el almuerzo?

EDUARDO: Me gusta comer papas y pollo.

MIRTA: Para el almuerzo, mi mamá tiene una ensalada, queso y pan. A nosotras nos gustan mucho las ensaladas.

EDUARDO: Hoy tengo mucha hambre y poca suerte.

[Each multiple-choice statement is given twice on the Test Cassette.]

1. Mirta va…
   a. a la tienda.
   b. a la escuela.
   c. a casa.

2. Eduardo va…
   a. a la casa de Alberto.
   b. a clase.
   c. al cine.

3. Alberto va a comer…
   a. pollo.
   b. legumbres.
   c. queso.

4. A Eduardo le gusta comer…
   a. pollo.
   b. ensalada.
   c. legumbres.

5. A Mirta le gustan…
   a. los huevos fritos.
   b. las papas.
   c. las ensaladas.

B. **Dictado.** Listen carefully to these sentences. You will hear each sentence twice. Write the missing words on the answer blanks.

[Each sentence is given twice on the Test Cassette. You may wish to pause the tape manually after each sentence has been repeated.]

1. Para el almuerzo quiero un sándwich.
2. Bueno. Tenemos uno de pollo.
3. ¿Hay ensalada de jamón?
4. No, pero hay ensalada de pescado.
5. Entonces como helado.

C. Now try writing these sentences for extra credit. You will hear each sentence twice.

[Read each of the following sentences twice.]

1. Te va a gustar la cena.
2. Primero vas a tomar sopa.
3. Es una sopa de plátano.
4. Luego vas a comer jamón.
5. También hay gelatina.

D. Listen carefully to these twelve words. You will hear each word twice. If you hear the hard sound of the consonant **c** in a word, circle **sí**. If you do not hear the hard sound of **c**, circle **no**. The first two have been done for you. (This test part is optional. Point values should not be applied to students' scores.)

1. caso, caso	5. gusto, gusto	9. suerte, suerte
2. sala, sala	6. contenta, contenta	10. cuchara, cuchara
3. cabeza, cabeza	7. carta, carta	11. sopa, sopa
4. cuando, cuando	8. garaje, garaje	12. coche, coche

UNIDAD 11: UNIT TEST [Test masters 125–126]

A. Listen to the conversation between Alicia, Gregorio, and their mother. Then you will hear five multiple-choice statements about their conversation. You will hear each statement twice. Circle the letter of the phrase that best completes each statement.

ALICIA:	Gregorio, tienes que levantarte. Es tarde.
GREGORIO:	¿Qué hora es?
MAMÁ:	Son las siete y media.
GREGORIO:	¡Ay! Sólo tengo treinta minutos para salir.
ALICIA:	Gregorio, yo me baño primero y me cepillo los dientes.
GREGORIO:	Yo me lavo la cara, me seco el pelo y me peino.
MAMÁ:	Ustedes también tienen que tomar el desayuno antes de irse.
GREGORIO:	Mamá, tengo prisa.
ALICIA:	Yo también tengo prisa.
MAMÁ:	¿Adónde van tan temprano?
ALICIA Y GREGORIO:	A la escuela. Las clases comienzan a las ocho.
MAMÁ:	¿A la escuela? Hoy es día de fiesta. No hay clases.

[Each multiple-choice statement is given twice on the Test Cassette.]

1. Gregorio está en…
   a. el baño.
   b. la cama.
   c. la escuela.

2. Son las…
   a. siete.
   b. siete y media.
   c. ocho.

3. Alicia va a…
   a. bañarse.
   b. acostarse.
   c. despertarse.

4. Gregorio va a…
   a. despertarse.
   b. lavarse la cara.
   c. acostarse.

5. Hoy es día de…
   a. escuela.
   b. trabajo.
   c. fiesta.

B. Dictado. Listen carefully to these sentences. You will hear each sentence twice. Write the missing words on the answer blanks.

[Each sentence is given twice on the Test Cassette. You may wish to pause the tape manually after each sentence has been repeated.]

1. Por la mañana me levanto temprano.
2. Luego me voy de la casa.
3. Las clases comienzan a las ocho.
4. Siempre estudio por la noche.
5. Aprendo mucho.

C. Now try writing these sentences for extra credit. You will hear each sentence twice.

[Read each of the following sentences twice.]

1. Vuelvo a la casa a las siete.
2. Primero me lavo las manos.
3. Luego como un poco.
4. Por último, me acuesto.
5. Me gusta dormir.

D. You will hear a number and a word. If the word has the sound of the letter **q** in it, circle the number. If the word does not have the sound of **q**, do not circle the number. The first two have been done for you. (This test part is optional. Point values should not be applied to students' scores.)

1.	queso	5.	cierras	9.	quitarse
2.	garaje	6.	pequeña	10.	querido
3.	que	7.	aquí	11.	guisantes
4.	techo	8.	cena	12.	guitarra

A. Listen to the conversation between Estela and Javier. Then you will hear five statements about their conversation. You will hear each statement twice. Circle **CIERTO** if the statement is true. Circle **FALSO** if it is false.

ESTELA:	Javier, ¿sabes dónde está el señor Fernández?
JAVIER:	Sí. El señor Fernández está en la biblioteca.
ESTELA:	No, en la biblioteca no hay nadie.
JAVIER:	¡Ah! Él está con la enfermera en la enfermería.
ESTELA:	No sé dónde está la enfermería.
JAVIER:	La enfermería está por el pasillo.
ESTELA:	¿Qué pasillo?
JAVIER:	El pasillo cerca de la cocina.
ESTELA:	No sé dónde está la cocina.
JAVIER:	Entonces, Estela, tienes que buscar un mapa primero.

¿Cierto o falso?

[Each statement is given twice on the Test Cassette.]

1. Estela busca a Javier.
2. El Sr. Fernández no está en la biblioteca.
3. Estela sabe dónde está la enfermería.
4. Javier sabe dónde está el pasillo.
5. Estela no sabe dónde está la cocina.

B. Dictado. Listen carefully to these sentences. You will hear each sentence twice. Write the missing words on the answer blanks.

[Each sentence is given twice on the Test Cassette. You may wish to pause the tape manually after each sentence has been repeated.]

1. El Sr. López trabaja en la escuela.
2. ¿Qué hace él?
3. Sabe hacer de todo.
4. ¿Es el director?
5. No, es el conserje.

C. Now try writing these sentences for extra credit. You will hear each sentence twice.

[Read each of the following sentences twice.]

1. Rosa es la más inteligente de todas.
2. ¿Es más inteligente que Ana?
3. Sí, mucho más inteligente.
4. ¿Cómo lo sabes?
5. ¡Es mi hermana!

D. Listen carefully to these twelve words. You will hear each word twice. If you hear the consonant **g** in a word, circle **sí**. If you do not hear the consonant **g**, circle **no**. The first two have been done for you. (This test part is optional. Point values should not be applied to students' scores.)

1. gana, gana
2. cama, cama
3. regalo, regalo
4. flamenco, flamenco

5. agosto, agosto
6. cuarto, cuarto
7. cosa, cosa
8. figura, figura

9. galón, galón
10. calor, calor
11. goma, goma
12. gusto, gusto

A. Listen to the conversation between Jaime and Sonia. Then you will hear five multiple-choice statements about their conversation. Circle the letter of the phrase that best completes each statement.

JAIME: ¡Hola, Sonia! ¿Qué tal?

SONIA: Bien, Jaime. ¿Y tú?

JAIME: Muy bien. Pienso nadar. ¿Quieres nadar conmigo?

SONIA: Es que…Mis papás no están en casa hoy. Mi hermanito José tiene que ir con nosotros.

JAIME: Bueno, ¿quieren ustedes nadar?

SONIA: No podemos. Mi hermanito no sabe nadar.

JAIME: ¿Pueden patinar?

SONIA: Yo sé patinar y me gusta mucho. Pero José no sabe patinar.

JAIME: Mmmm. ¿Quieren ustedes bailar? Hay un baile en la escuela esta tarde.

SONIA: Lo siento. José tampoco sabe bailar.

JAIME: Pues, podemos ir a mi casa a almorzar.

SONIA: ¡Qué buena idea! ¡José sí sabe comer!

1. Sonia está…
  a. regular.
  b. mal.
  c. bien.

2. Jaime piensa…
  a. nadar.
  b. comer.
  c. estudiar.

3. Los padres de Sonia…
  a. no nadan.
  b. no están.
  c. no almuerzan.

4. José es el…
  a. papá.
  b. amigo.
  c. hermanito.

5. José sabe…
  a. nadar.
  b. bailar.
  c. comer.

B. Dictado. Listen carefully to these sentences. You will hear each sentence twice. Write the missing words on the answer blanks.

[Each sentence is given twice on the Test Cassette. You may wish to pause the tape manually after each sentence has been repeated.]

1. ¿Cuando comienzas a estudiar?

2. Comienzo a las nueve.

3. ¿Te gusta estudiar tarde?

4. Claro que sí.

5. A mí no.

C. Listen carefully to these twelve words. You will hear each word twice. Complete each word by writing a vowel or consonant letter on the answer blank. The first two have been done for you. (This test part is optional. Point values should not be applied to students' scores.)

1. mes, mes

2. sala, sala

3. ahora, ahora

4. hijo, hijo

5. enero, enero

6. abajo, abajo

7. niño, niño

8. querido, querido

9. cereza, cereza

10. rubia, rubia

11. cerrar, cerrar

12. doña, doña

ANSWER KEY

In this section, you will find the answers to all the tests in the *¿Qué tal? Testing Program* blackline master book. For each test, the following information is given: the test blackline master numbers, the total points for the test, and the section-by-section and part-by-part breakdown of points.

In addition, the levels of difficulty are provided for the unit tests, the achievement review tests, and the Mid-Year Test:

○ Lowest level of difficulty

◑ Average level of difficulty

● Highest level of difficulty

The following symbols are given for your information:

★ Extra credit

  Test Cassette

The complete tapescript for the Test Cassette is included in this *Testing Program* book in the section "Oral Test Tapescript and Guide." Also in that section you will find the information, or script, you will need to administer the Speaking Section of the Placement Test and the extra-credit parts in Section 3 of the unit tests (see pages T-24 to T-60).

PLACEMENT TEST

(Test masters 1–8)

Total points: 60 / Total optional points: 10

Section 1
(15 points)

A. (5 points)
1. b (Son unas medias.) *(model)*
2. d (Ella toca la nariz.)
3. f (Luis plancha la ropa.)
4. a (Es mi ropero.)
5. e (El lavaplatos es nuevo.)
6. c (Un cuarto de baño está
        cerca.)

B. (5 points)
1. pan *(model)*
2. zanahorias
3. fritos
4. sandía
5. leche
6. nadie

C. (5 points)
1. fuerte *(model)*
2. falda
3. pies
4. enfermera
5. atlética
6. quita

Section 2
(20 points)

A. (5 points)
1. les
2. ti
3. Tus
4. se
5. ellas

B. (15 points)
1. puede
2. llevan
3. comienzan
4. te peinas
5. sé
6. quieren
7. trae
8. acaba
9. cocinan
10. vivimos
11. Están
12. son
13. duele
14. quedan
15. cerramos

Section 3
(25 points)

A. (5 points)
1. b (Pablo tiene *un problema*.)
2. c (Roberto sólo quiere hablar
        de *su desayuno*.)
3. c (Cecilia sólo quiere hablar
        de *matemáticas*.)
4. a (David sólo quiere hablar
        de *su casa*.)
5. b (El papá de Pablo *dice*
        "*adiós*.")

B. (10 points)
1. dueña / compañía
2. almorzamos / ella
3. Vive lejos de aquí.
4. Cocina muy bien.
5. Siempre sirve algo bueno.

C. Speaking (10 points)

Answers will vary.

D. (10 optional points)
1. m<u>e</u>sa *(model)*
2. <u>s</u>al *(model)*
3. <u>j</u>ueves
4. h<u>i</u>ja
5. <u>ll</u>evar
6. po<u>ll</u>o
7. <u>n</u>oche
8. <u>q</u>ueso
9. s<u>u</u>cia
10. <u>r</u>ubio
11. <u>c</u>erca
12. <u>g</u>uerra

(Test masters 9–14)

Total points: 50 / Total extra credit points: 10 / Total optional points: 10

Section 1

(15 points)

A. (10 points) ○
1. h (el pelo) *(model)*
2. c (la cabeza)
3. a (la boca)
4. e (el codo)
5. g (la mano)
6. f (los dedos)
7. j (el pie)
8. k (la rodilla)
9. i (la pierna)
10. d (la cintura)
11. b (el brazo)

B. (5 points) ◑
1. la frente *(model)*
2. la ceja
3. el ojo
4. la oreja
5. la nariz
6. la mejilla

Section 2

(20 points; 5 points extra credit)

A. (10 points) ○
1. duelen
2. duele
3. duelen
4. duelen
5. duele
6. duele
7. duele
8. duelen
9. duele
10. duelen

B. (10 points) ◑

En <u>la</u> *(model)* cabeza está <u>el</u> pelo. En <u>la</u> frente están <u>las</u> cejas. <u>Los</u> ojos y <u>la</u> nariz están en <u>la</u> cara. <u>La</u> boca tiene <u>los</u> labios, <u>los</u> dientes y <u>la</u> lengua.

C. (5 points) ● ★
a. ¿Qué de duele —— a ella? *(model)* / a él? / a Rita? / a usted?
b. ¿Qué te duele —— a ti?
c. ¿Qué me duele —— a mí?

Section 3

(15 points; 5 points extra credit)

A. (5 points) ◑
1. b (Son las siete y media *de la mañana*.)
2. c (Víctor tiene *un examen*.)
3. c Es un examen de *historia*.)
4. c (Víctor va *a la escuela*.)
5. b (Víctor va *ahora mismo*.)

B. (10 points) ◑

PAPÁ:
¿<u>Qué</u> te duele, Carlitos?
CARLITOS:
Me duele <u>la cabeza</u>.
PAPÁ:
¿<u>Cuánto</u> y <u>cuándo</u> te duele?
CARLITOS:
Me duele <u>mucho</u> los <u>viernes</u> a las <u>siete</u> de la <u>mañana</u> porque tengo clase de <u>ciencias</u>.

C. (5 points) ● ★
1. No estoy bien de salud.
2. Tengo los ojos rojos.
3. Tengo dolor de cabeza.
4. Me duele el cuerpo.
5. Tienes la gripe.

D. (10 optional points) ○
1. bu<u>e</u>no *(model)*
2. a<u>ñ</u>o *(model)*
3. pu<u>n</u>to
4. sue<u>ñ</u>o
5. ni<u>ñ</u>o
6. ma<u>n</u>o
7. <u>n</u>ietos
8. espa<u>ñ</u>ol
9. i<u>n</u>glés
10. ci<u>n</u>tura
11. do<u>ñ</u>a
12. ju<u>n</u>io

UNIDAD 2: UNIT TEST

(Test masters 15–22)

Total points: 50 / Total extra credit points: 10 / Total optional points: 10

Section 1

(15 points)

A. (6 points) ○
1. una chaqueta.
2. una camisa.
3. unos pantalones.
4. un vestido.
5. una blusa.
6. una falda.

B. (6 points) ◑
1. el impermeable
2. la camiseta
3. el traje de baño
4. los zapatos
5. el abrigo
6. las botas

C. (3 points) ◑
1. grande
2. mediana
3. pequeña

Section 2

(20 points; 5 points extra credit)

A. (6 points) ○
1. queda
2. quedan
3. quedan
4. queda
5. queda
6. quedan

B. (6 points) ◑
1. b (corto.)
2. a (bonita.)
3. b (feas.)

4. c (pequeños.)
5. a (corta.)
6. c (largo.)

C. (8 points) ◑
1. del *(model)*
2. de la
3. de él
4. del
5. de las
6. de los
7. de la
8. de él
9. del

D. (5 points) ● ★
1. P: ¿Qué ropa llevas en enero?
   (model)
   R: Yo llevo un abrigo.
2. P: ¿Cómo es el abrigo?
   R: Es grande.
3. P: ¿De quién son las botas?
   R: Son de mi hermana.
   Mañana y voy a llevar sus botas.

Section 3

(15 points; 5 points extra credit)

A. (5 points) ◑
1. Falso
2. Cierto
3. Falso
4. Cierto
5. Cierto

B. (10 points) ◑
RAÚL:
¿Dónde está mi ropa de verano?

MAMÁ:
No tienes.
RAÚL:
¿De quién es la chaqueta? Es bonita.
MAMÁ:
Es de tu hermano Carlos. Te queda pequeña.
RAÚL:
¿De quién es el sombrero?
MAMÁ:
Es de tu primo Pedro.
RAÚL:
¿Y los zapatos? ¡Son feos!
MAMÁ:
Son tus zapatos nuevos para ir a la escuela.

C. (5 points) ● ★
1. Paula tiene ojos bonitos.
2. Tiene el pelo negro.
3. Su vestido es fantástico.
4. Tiene una carita muy bonita.
5. Paula es una niña de doce días.

D. (10 optional points) ○
1. sí (hija) *(model)*
2. no (oreja) *(model)*
3. sí (ahora)
4. no (loro)
5. no (ojo)
6. sí (historia)
7. sí (hermano)
8. sí (hace)
9. no (ceja)
10. sí (hay)
11. sí (hermana)
12. no (cara)

UNIDAD 3: UNIT TEST

(Test masters 23–30)
Total points: 50 / Total extra credit points: 10 / Total optional points: 10

Section 1
(15 points)

A. (5 points) ○
1. delgado *(model)*
2. grueso
3. baja
4. alta
5. débil
6. fuerte

B. (7 points) ◑
1. inteligente *(model)*
2. cómica
3. popular
4. generoso
5. atlética
6. tímido
7. simpático
8. impaciente

C. (3 points) ◑
1. lacio
2. ondulado
3. rizado

Section 2
(20 points; 5 points extra credit)

A. (8 points) ○
1. es *(model)*
2. es
3. eres
4. es
5. son
6. son
7. eres
8. soy
9. es

B. (12 points) ◑
1. Lupe es <u>más alta</u> que Pilar.
   Pilar es <u>menos alta</u> que Lupe.
2. Tu gato es <u>menos grande</u> que mi gato.
   Mi gato es <u>más grande</u> que tu gato.
3. Ema es <u>menos delgada</u> que Anita.
   Anita es <u>más delgada</u> que Ema.

C. (5 points) ◑ ★
1. eres
2. son
3. es
4. son
5. soy

Section 3
(15 points; 5 points extra credit)

A. (5 points) ◑
1. b (Los ojos de Enrique son *castaños.*)
2. a (Enrique tiene el pelo *rojizo.*)
3. c (Manuel es *delgado.*)
4. b (Gertrudis es *alta.*)
5. c (Gertrudis también es *gruesa.*)

B. (10 points) ◑
1. qué / color
2. Tengo / castaños
3. Cómo / mamá
4. grandes / mis
5. Ella / verdes

C. (5 points) ● ★
1. Yo soy más alta que Ana.
2. Ana es menos alta que María.
3. María es menos alta que yo.
4. Sara es más alta que yo.
5. ¿Es Ana más alta que Sara?

D. (10 optional points) ○
1. <u>b</u>ajo *(model)*
2. a<u>b</u>ajo *(model)*
3. <u>v</u>erano *(model)*
4. prima<u>v</u>era *(model)*
5. <u>v</u>erdad
6. a<u>b</u>rigo
7. <u>b</u>lusa
8. no<u>v</u>iembre
9. a<u>b</u>uela
10. <u>v</u>as
11. ca<u>b</u>eza
12. <u>b</u>otas
13. di<u>v</u>ertido
14. <u>v</u>einte

REPASO: UNIDADES 1–3 ACHIEVEMENT REVIEW TEST

(Test masters 31–36)

Total points: 40 / Total optional points: 10

Section 1
(10 points)

A. (5 points) ○
1. ceja *(model)*
2. pantalones
3. débil
4. popular
5. feo
6. espalda

B. (5 points) ●
1. impaciente *(model)*
2. baño
3. oreja
4. dientes
5. camisa
6. rizado

Section 2
(15 points)

A. (6 points) ◑
1. queda / corta
2. queda / pequeña
3. quedan / largas

B. (4 points) ○
1. el ojo
2. el diente
3. las piernas
4. las pestañas

C. (5 points) ○
1. menos
2. menos
3. más
4. menos
5. más

Section 3
(15 points)

A. (5 points) ○ 🎞
1. Cierto
2. Falso
3. Falso
4. Cierto
5. Falso

B. (10 points) ◑ 🎞
1. Cómo / tu
2. hermana / generosa
3. pelo / rubio
4. Sus ojos son bonitos.
5. Yo soy más baja que ella.

C. (10 optional points) ○ 🎞
1. u̲na *(model)*
2. h̲umano *(model)*
3. españo̲l
4. h̲ijo
5. b̲año
6. v̲entana
7. h̲istoria
8. añ̲o
9. n̲egro
10. doñ̲a
11. b̲oca
12. v̲estido

UNIDAD 4: UNIT TEST

(Test masters 37–44)

Total points: 50 / Total extra credit points: 10 / Total optional points: 10

Section 1

(15 points)

A. (6 points) ○
1. c (la chimenea) *(model)*
2. h (el techo)
3. g (el patio)
4. e (el garaje)
5. d (las escaleras)
6. b (el buzón)
7. f (el jardín)

B. (6 points) ◐
1. comedor
2. cuarto de baño
3. cocina
4. despacho
5. sala
6. dormitorio

C. (3 points) ○
1. dentro
2. fuera
3. dentro

Section 2

(20 points; 5 points extra credit)

A. (7 points) ○
1. están
2. está
3. estás
4. estoy
5. estás
6. están
7. estamos

B. (5 points) ◐
1. yo *(model)*
2. ellas
3. ella
4. ellos
5. él
6. ustedes

C. (8 points) ●
1. ellos
2. nosotros
3. ellas
4. ellos
5. ustedes
6. ellas
7. ustedes
8. nosotras

D. (5 points) ● ★
1. fuera de
2. dentro de
3. dentro de
4. fuera de
5. dentro de

Section 3

(15 points; 5 points extra credit)

A. (5 points) ◐ 📼
1. Cierto
2. Falso
3. Cierto
4. Falso
5. Cierto

B. (10 points) ◐ 📼
1. Cómo / casa
2. muy / grande
3. Tiene / dormitorios
4. ¿Hay garaje?
5. Sí. Tiene patio también.

C. (5 points) ● ★
1. ¿Dónde está Elena?
2. Está dentro de la casa.
3. ¿En qué cuarto está?
4. Está en su dormitorio.
5. Siempre estudia en su cuarto.

D. (10 optional points) ○ 📼
1. p_atio *(model)*
2. bu_zón *(model)*
3. sót_ano
4. coc_ina
5. d_ormitorio
6. d_entro
7. _ustedes
8. balcon_es
9. despach_o
10. _una
11. _garaje
12. ch_imenea

UNIDAD 5: UNIT TEST

(Test masters 45–54)

Total points: 50 / Total extra credit points: 10 / Total optional points: 10

Section 1

(15 points)

A. (5 points) ○
1. c (Hay una alfombra en el piso.) *(model)*
2. b (Hay una lámpara.)
3. f (Hay un televisor.)
4. e (Hay un sofá grande.)
5. a (Hay cortinas.)
6. d (Hay un retrato de la familia.)

B. (5 points) ◐
1. en un sillón *(model)*
2. de la lámpara
3. del sofá
4. del estante
5. del equipo de sonido
6. del espejo

C. (5 points) ●
1. radio *(model)*
2. cama
3. almohada
4. ropero
5. cartel
6. teléfono

Section 2

(20 points; 5 points extra credit)

A. (8 points) ◐
1. delante de
2. detrás de
3. cerca del
4. lejos de

5. delante de
6. lejos de
7. detrás del
8. lejos del

B. (12 points) ◐
1. alumnas / bonitas
2. carteles / feos
3. manos / delgadas
4. lápices / azules
5. mapas / grandes
6. sofás / amarillos

C. (5 points) ● ★
1. El estante es largo.
2. El teléfono azul está cerca de la pared.
3. Hay un tocador alto.
4. Una mujer es simpática.
5. ¿Es grande la mano?

Section 3

(15 points; 5 points extra credit)

A. (5 points) ◐
1. b. (Esteban tiene *un televisor*.)
2. c (El señor Olvida habla con *un muchacho y una muchacha*.)
3. c (El televisor va *en el piso*.)
4. b (A Raquel le duelen *los brazos*.)
5. b (Raquel y Esteban dicen "adiós" *al señor Olvida*.)

B. (10 points) ◐
1. Cómo / sala
2. y / muebles
3. Cuántos / sillones
4. Hay un sillón y un sofá.
5. ¿El piso tiene alfombra?

C. (5 points) ● ★
1. ¿Dónde está el televisor?
2. Está en la sala.
3. ¿Tiene usted radio?
4. Sí, está en el estante.
5. ¿Hay teléfono aquí?

D. (10 optional points) ○
1. (cortina) *(model)*
2. (alta) *(model)*
3. (caro)
4. (lámpara)
5. (delante)
6. (detrás)
7. (anda)
8. (tengo)
9. (Mario)
10. (tímido)
11. (bonito)
12. (madre)

(Test masters 55–63)

Total points: 50 / Total extra credit points: 10 / Total optional points: 10

Section 1

(15 points)

A. (8 points) ○
1. f (el horno)
2. g (el horno de microondas)
3. c (la estufa)
4. a (el abrelatas)
5. e (la licuadora)
6. h (el lavaplatos)
7. b (la batidora eléctrica)
8. i (la bombilla)

B. (7 points) ●
1. licuadora *(model)*
2. caja
3. bol
4. grifo
5. cajón
6. refrigerador
7. lata
8. tostador

Section 2

(20 points; 5 points extra credit)

A. (10 points) ◑
1. Comemos
2. cocina
3. usa
4. Uso
5. Aprendes
6. caminan
7. escribe
8. leen
9. abre
10. miramos

B. (10 points) ◑
1. vive
2. corren
3. bailan
4. camino
5. escribimos
6. abre
7. pinta
8. comprende
9. usamos
10. comen

C. (5 points) ● ★

Estimado profesor:

En el salón de clase sólo hay dos computadoras. Por lo general, los viernes a las cinco de la tarde, yo <u>uso</u> la computadora nueva. Juan y Marta también <u>usan</u> la computadora nueva los viernes por la tarde. A veces Juan, Marta y yo <u>usamos</u> la vieja. ¿Hay posibilidad de usar yo la computadora nueva mañana a las cinco de la tarde? Si mañana usted y los alumnos <u>usan</u> las computadoras, me voy y <u>uso</u> la computadora de un amigo.

Atentamente,
Samuel

Section 3

(15 points; 5 points extra credit)

A. (5 points) ◑
1. Cierto
2. Falso
3. Falso
4. Cierto
5. Cierto

B. (10 points) ◑
1. tu / cocinan
2. yo / cocino
3. horno / microondas
4. usamos / lavaplatos
5. batidora eléctrica

C. (5 points) ● ★
1. ¿Qué te gusta hacer?
2. Me gusta leer.
3. ¿Estudias ahora?
4. Mi hermano y yo estudiamos.
5. ¿Abro el libro?

D. (10 optional points) ○
1. sí (corre) *(model)*
2. no (luego) *(model)*
3. sí (rica)
4. no (ustedes)
5. sí (arroz)
6. sí (borrador)
7. no (estufa)
8. sí (carro)
9. no (¿cuántos?)
10. no (paredes)
11. sí (ropero)
12. no (baila)

(Test masters 64–70)

Total points: 40 / Total optional points: 10

Section 1

(10 points)

A. (5 points) ○
1. garaje *(model)*
2. estante
3. piso
4. estufa
5. cocina
6. enchufe

B. (5 points) ●
1. comedor *(model)*
2. lavaplatos
3. retrato
4. buzón
5. abrelatas
6. espejo

Section 2

(15 points)

A. (4 points) ○
1. fuera de
2. dentro de
3. detrás de
4. delante de

B. (6 points) ◑
1. alumnos / grandes
2. paredes / altas
3. mapas / pequeños

C. (5 points) ●
1. está
2. estamos
3. pinto
4. leen
5. viven

Section 3

(15 points)

A. (5 points) ◑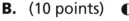
1. b (Pedro y Felipe están *en la sala*.)
2. a (Alma está en *el patio*.)
3. c (El tío de Pedro se llama *Javier*.)
4. c (Al tío de Pedro le gusta mucho *pintar*.)
5. a (Pedro abre *las cortinas*.)

B. (10 points) ◑
1. verano / comemos
2. detrás / casa
3. gusta / cocinar
4. Mi hermana come mucho.
5. Mis hermanos cocinan bien.

C. (10 optional points) ○
1. están *(model)*
2. ropa *(model)*
3. biblioteca
4. trabajo
5. perro
6. sucio
7. vida
8. tomar
9. mujer
10. techo
11. río
12. alfombra

(Test masters 71–78)

Total points: 50 / Total optional points: 10

Section 1
(15 points)

A. (5 points) ○
1. c (Mi casa tiene sótano.) *(model)*
2. b (Hay un despacho.)
3. f (Es el sillón de mi papá.)
4. d (En el dormitorio hay un espejo.)
5. a (Es el techo de la casa.)
6. e (Tenemos un televisor grande.)

B. (5 points) ◑
1. estufa *(model)*
2. dedos
3. licuadora
4. enchufe
5. gorra
6. ondulado

C. (5 points) ●
1. cómica *(model)*
2. simpático
3. pijama
4. cuerpo
5. oreja
6. bata

Section 2
(20 points)

A. (10 points) ◑
1. camina
2. aprenden
3. escribe
4. miran
5. Está
6. comemos
7. duelen
8. quedan
9. estamos
10. abren

B. (10 points) ●
1. Los niños son pequeños. *(model)*
2. Las señoras son altas.
3. Los sombreros son feos.
4. Tus paredes son amarillas.
5. Sus lápices son rojos.
6. Los mapas son grandes.

Section 3
(15 points)

A. (5 points) ◑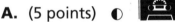
1. b (La familia de Manuel vive en *una casa*.)
2. a (La cocina tiene *un refrigerador*.)
3. c (El comedor es *grande*.)
4. b (El dormitorio de Manuel tiene *dos ventanas*.)
5. b (A Manuel le duelen *los pies*.)

B. (10 points) ◑
1. cerca / aquí
2. casa / lejos
3. Cómo / patio
4. Es muy grande.
5. Está detrás de la casa.

C. (10 optional points) ○
1. c<u>a</u>si *(model)*
2. ense<u>ñ</u>a *(model)*
3. <u>h</u>otel
4. m<u>e</u>sa
5. <u>v</u>aca
6. <u>l</u>oro
7. <u>l</u>ugar
8. <u>n</u>acho
9. <u>h</u>ablar
10. pi<u>ñ</u>a
11. ci<u>n</u>e
12. tam<u>b</u>ién

UNIDAD 7: UNIT TEST

(Test masters 79–86)

Total points: 50 / Total extra credit points: 10 / Total optional points: 10

Section 1

(15 points)

A. (10 points) ◑

1. Limpio / trapeador
2. Plancho / plancha
3. Quito / trapo
4. Barro / escoba
5. Seco / secadora

B. (5 points) ●

1. Mi ropa está sucia. —— Voy a lavar mi ropa. *(model)*
2. La alfombra está limpia. —— No voy a pasar la aspiradora. *(model)*
3. Tu ropa está limpia. —— No voy a lavar tu ropa.
4. Hay mucha basura. —— Voy a sacar la basura.
5. La alfombra está sucia. —— Voy a pasar la aspiradora.
6. Hay mucho polvo en el tocador. —— Voy a quitar el polvo.
7. El piso está limpio. —— No voy a barrer el piso.

Section 2

(20 points; 5 points extra credit)

A. (10 points) ○

1. tienes que
2. tengo que
3. tenemos que
4. tienen que
5. tiene que

6. tiene que
7. tienes que
8. tiene que
9. tienen que
10. tengo que

B. (10 points) ◑

1. acaba de
2. acaba de
3. acaban de
4. acaba de
5. acabas de
6. acabo de
7. acabas de
8. acaba de
9. acabamos de
10. acaban de

C. (5 points) ● ★

¡Hola mamá! Acabo <u>de</u> *(model)* estudiar matemáticas <u>con</u> Carlos. Ahora tengo <u>que</u> estudiar español <u>con</u> Elena y Mirta. Luego, Ana y yo tenemos <u>que</u> estudiar ciencias. ¡Caramba! ¡Acaban <u>de</u> llegar Elena, Mirta y Ana!

Section 3

(15 points; 5 points extra credit)

A. (5 points) ◑

1. Falso
2. Cierto
3. Cierto
4. Falso
5. Cierto

B. (10 points) ◑ 🔊

1. tienes / casa
2. tengo / pisos
3. lava / ropa
4. Mi hermano quita el polvo.
5. Mi papá seca la ropa.

C. (5 points) ● ★

1. Acabo de limpiar la cocina.
2. ¿Qué acaba de hacer Raúl?
3. Acaba de recoger la ropa.
4. ¿Qué acaban de hacer ustedes?
5. Acabamos de lavar los platos.

D. (10 optional points) ○ 🔊

1. ca<u>r</u>o *(model)*
2. ca<u>rr</u>o *(model)*
3. pe<u>rr</u>o
4. pe<u>r</u>o
5. habla<u>r</u>
6. <u>r</u>opa
7. saca<u>r</u>
8. ca<u>r</u>ta
9. <u>r</u>eloj
10. a<u>rr</u>iba
11. <u>r</u>ápido
12. basu<u>r</u>a

UNIDAD 8: UNIT TEST

(Test masters 87–94)

Total points: 50 / Total extra credit points: 10 / Total optional points: 10

Section 1

(15 points)

A. (8 points) ○
1. la sal
2. el azúcar
3. los vasos
4. las servilletas
5. la crema
6. la pimienta
7. los platos
8. las tazas

B. (7 points) ◑
1. la sandía
2. las cerezas
3. las manzanas
4. las uvas
5. la piña
6. los plátanos
7. las peras

Section 2

(20 points; 5 points extra credit)

A. (8 points) ○
1. ponemos
2. pone
3. pongo
4. pones
5. ponen
6. pones
7. ponen
8. ponemos

B. (9 points) ◑
1. trae
2. traigo
3. traes
4. traen
5. trae
6. traen
7. traemos
8. traen
9. trae

C. (3 points) ◑
1. debajo de
2. debajo del
3. sobre

D. (5 points) ● ★

Para la fiesta, yo <u>traigo</u> las sillas y tú <u>traes</u> el mantel. Alma <u>trae</u> a sus dos primos. Si tú <u>pones</u> la mesa, yo <u>pongo</u> las flores.

Section 3

(15 points; 5 points extra credit)

A. (5 points) ◑
1. b (Juan está *así, así.*)
2. a (Cecilia va a *comer frutas.*)
3. c (A Cecilia le gustan mucho las manzanas, las uvas y las *fresas.*)
4. a (A Juan no le gusta *la sandía.*)
5. a (Ahora, Juan ya no tiene *hambre.*)

B. (10 points) ◑
1. poner / mesa
2. azúcar / crema
3. sal / pimienta
4. Luisa pone las servilletas.
5. Yo pongo el mantel.

C. (5 points) ● ★
1. ¿Qué frutas traen ustedes?
2. Yo traigo naranjas.
3. Celia trae la sandía.
4. Ricardo trae manzanas.
5. Catalina trae uvas.

D. (10 optional points) ○
1. mú<u>s</u>ica *(model)*
2. <u>z</u>apato *(model)*
3. pi<u>z</u>arra
4. gu<u>s</u>to
5. ha<u>s</u>ta
6. mar<u>z</u>o
7. e<u>s</u>cribe
8. ago<u>s</u>to
9. a<u>z</u>ul
10. co<u>s</u>a
11. bu<u>z</u>ón
12. <u>z</u>oológico

(Test masters 95–103)

Total points: 50 / Total extra credit points: 10 / Total optional points: 10

Section 1

(15 points)

A. (10 points) ◑
1. cereal
2. jugo
3. huevos fritos
4. té
5. pan tostado
6. leche
7. avena
8. chocolate
9. toronja
10. mermelada

B. (5 points) ◑
1. querer *(model)*
2. desayuno
3. huevos pasados por agua
4. beber
5. huevos revueltos
6. margarina

Section 2

(20 points; 5 points extra credit)

A. (5 points) ◑
1. nuestro
2. nuestros
3. nuestra
4. nuestras
5. nuestra

B. (10 points) ◑
1. quiero
2. quieres
3. queremos

4. quiere
5. quieren
6. quieren
7. quiere
8. queremos
9. quieren
10. quiere

C. (5 points) ◑
1. nuevo *(model)*
2. viejas *(model)*
3. vieja
4. nuevos
5. nueva
6. viejos
7. nuevo

D. (5 points) ● ★
1. Tu
2. Su
3. Tu
4. Tus
5. Sus

Section 3

(15 points; 5 points extra credit)

A. (5 points) ◑
1. Cierto
2. Falso
3. Falso
4. Cierto
5. Cierto

B. (10 points) ◑
1. quieres / desayuno
2. quiero / pasados
3. quiere / cereal
4. ¿Qué jugo toman?
5. Tomamos jugo de naranja.

C. (5 points) ● ★
1. ¿Es nueva tu casa?
2. No, mi casa es vieja.
3. ¿Son nuevos tus muebles?
4. Los muebles son de mis papás.
5. ¿Son nuevos sus muebles?

D. (10 optional points) ○
1. (centro)   *(model)*
2. (cinco)   *(model)*
3. (cuatro)   *(model)*
4. (tocino)
5. (once)
6. (quiero)
7. (nunca)
8. (veces)
9. (cuarto)
10. (trece)
11. (difícil)
12. (cine)
13. (cereza)

REPASO: UNIDADES 7–9 ACHIEVEMENT REVIEW TEST

(Test masters 104–109)

Total points: 40 / Total optional points: 10

Section 1
(10 points)

A. (5 points) ◑
1. jugo *(model)*
2. tenedor
3. té
4. servilleta
5. secar
6. sacar

B. (5 points) ●
1. escoba *(model)*
2. plancha
3. uvas
4. cerezas
5. revueltos
6. cereal

Section 2
(15 points)

A. (4 points) ◑

SARA:
Mamá, yo <u>acabo</u> *(model)* de recibir una "D" en ciencias.

MAMÁ:
Sara, tú <u>tienes</u> que estudiar más.

SARA:
Pero, mamá, yo <u>traigo</u> mis libros a casa todos los días…

MAMÁ:
Yo comprendo, Sara. Mañana tú y yo <u>ponemos</u> el reloj para las seis de la mañana. Tu hermano también <u>quiere</u> estudiar temprano.

B. (6 points) ◑

JUAN:
¿El gato acaba <u>de</u> salir? *(model)*

INÉS:
No, el gato tiene <u>que</u> estar <u>en</u> la casa.

JUAN:
¿El gato está <u>con</u> Ana?

INÉS:
No, Ana no está <u>en</u> la casa.

JUAN:
¿El gato está <u>sobre</u> la mesa?

INÉS:
No. ¡El gato está en el piso, <u>debajo de</u> la mesa!

C. (5 points) ◑
1. su
2. tu
3. nuestro
4. nuestros
5. nuestras

Section 3
(15 points)

A. (5 points) ◑
1. c (Rita acaba de *poner la mesa*.)
2. a (Rubén acaba de *comer*.)
3. a (Rubén tiene que limpiar *el garaje*.)
4. b (Para el desayuno, Rita trae *toronjas*.)
5. b (Rita tiene que poner un plato más porque Rubén tiene *hambre*.)

B. (10 points) ◑
1. Dónde / mi
2. debajo / mesa
3. Tu / tiene
4. El perrito no quiere nada.
5. Él acaba de comer mucho.

C. (10 optional points) ○
1. pe<u>r</u>a *(model)*
2. <u>s</u>ofá *(model)*
3. pe<u>rr</u>o
4. <u>z</u>apato
5. <u>c</u>erca
6. <u>r</u>adio
7. ta<u>z</u>a
8. <u>c</u>ereal
9. pa<u>s</u>ados
10. po<u>r</u>que
11. ve<u>c</u>es
12. co<u>rr</u>e

UNIDAD 10: UNIT TEST

(Test masters 110–118)

Total points: 50 / Total extra credit points: 10 / Total optional points: 10

Section 1

(15 points)

A. (5 points) ○
1. pan *(model)*
2. legumbres
3. queso
4. pollo
5. papas
6. hamburguesa

B. (6 points) ◑
1. el pavo
2. el pescado
3. el arroz
4. la carne
5. las zanahorias
6. los guisantes

C. (4 points) ◑

LUIS:
Ana, es mediodía. ¿Quieres <u>comer</u>? *(model)*

ANA:
No, gracias. No quiero <u>almorzar</u> ahora.

LUIS:
Vamos, Ana. ¿Quieres <u>probar</u> el jugo de zanahoria? A ti te va a <u>gustar</u> mucho.

ANA:
Ahora no puedo. ¿Vas a <u>poder</u> tomar la cena en mi casa esta noche?

LUIS:
Sí. Puedo ir a tu casa a las ocho.

Section 2

(20 points; 5 points extra credit)

A. (8 points) ◐
1. almuerzo
2. almuerza
3. almuerzan
4. almuerzas
5. almuerza
6. almorzamos
7. almorzamos
8. almuerzan

B. (7 points) ◐
1. mí *(model)*
2. ellos *(model)*
3. ellas
4. ustedes
5. mí
6. él
7. ellas
8. nosotros (OR nosotras)
9. ti

C. (5 points) ◐

RAMONA:
Enrique, ¿<u>puedes</u> *(model)* almorzar conmigo?

ENRIQUE:
Lo siento Ramona, no <u>puedo</u>. Tengo que estudiar con Ricardo.

RAMONA:
Bueno. ¿Entonces tú <u>puedes</u> cenar con mi familia esta noche? Mi papá cocina muy bien.

ENRIQUE:
Hmm. ¿Ricardo también <u>puede</u> ir?

RAMONA:
¡Cómo no! Todos <u>podemos</u> cenar. ¿A qué hora <u>pueden</u> ustedes estar en mi casa?

ENRIQUE:
¿A las siete en punto?

RAMONA:
De acuerdo. Hasta luego, Enrique.

D. (5 points) ● ★

MAMÁ:
Pepe, ¿a <u>ti</u> te gusta el arroz?

PEPE:
No, mamá, no <u>me</u> gusta.

MAMÁ:
¿Te <u>gustan</u> las papas?

PEPE:
No, mamá.

MAMÁ:
Entonces, Pepe, ¿qué <u>te</u> gusta?

PEPE:
Mamá, yo soy como Popeye. ¡A <u>mí</u> me gustan las espinacas!

Section 3

(15 points; 5 points extra credit)

A. (5 points) ◐ 🚗
1. c (Mirta va *a casa.*)
2. a (Eduardo va *a la casa de Alberto.*)
3. b (Alberto va a comer *legumbres.*)
4. a (A Eduardo le gusta comer *pollo.*)
5. c (A Mirta le gustan *las ensaladas.*)

B. (10 points) ◑ 🔊

1. almuerzo / sándwich
2. Tenemos / pollo
3. ensalada / jamón
4. No, pero hay ensalada de pescado.
5. Entonces como helado.

C. (5 points) ● ★

1. Te va a gustar la cena.
2. Primero vas a tomar sopa.
3. Es una sopa de plátano.
4. Luego vas a comer jamón.
5. También hay gelatina.

D. (10 optional points) ○ 🔊

1. sí (caso)   *(model)*
2. no (sala)   *(model)*
3. sí (cabeza)
4. sí (cuando)
5. no (gusto)
6. sí (contenta)
7. sí (carta)
8. no (garaje)
9. no (suerte)
10. sí (cuchara)
11. no (sopa)
12. sí (coche)

(Test masters 119–126)

Total points: 50 / Total extra credit points: 10 / Total optional points: 10

Section 1

(15 points)

A. (11 points) ○
1. despertarse *(model)*
2. levantarse
3. cepillarse
4. lavarse
5. secarse
6. ponerse
7. peinarse
8. irse
9. volver
10. quitarse
11. bañarse
12. acostarse

B. (4 points) ●
1. bien *(model)*
2. Primero me despierto y luego me levanto. *(model)*
3. Primero me quito la ropa y luego me baño.
4. bien
5. bien
6. Primero me lavo la cara y luego me seco.

Section 2

(20 points; 5 points extra credit)

A. (10 points) ○
1. se lava
2. me baño
3. nos cepillamos
4. se peinan
5. te bañas
6. se levanta
7. te acuestas
8. se ponen
9. nos despertamos
10. me acuesto

B. (10 points) ◑
1. pienso
2. piensa
3. piensan
4. piensas
5. piensa
6. pensamos
7. piensas
8. piensan
9. pensamos
10. pienso

C. (5 points) ● ★

<u>Nos</u> vamos a las siete. Yo <u>me</u> pongo el vestido azul. Como va a hacer frío, <u>me</u> pongo el abrigo. Catalina <u>se</u> pone una falda verde. María y Alicia <u>se</u> ponen pantalones.

Section 3

(15 points; 5 points extra credit)

A. (5 points) ◑
1. b (Gregorio está en *la cama*).
2. b (Son las *siete y media*.)
3. a (Alicia va a *bañarse*).
4. b (Gregorio va a *lavarse la cara*.)
5. c (Hoy es día de *fiesta*.)

B. (10 points) ◑
1. Por / me levanto
2. Luego / me voy
3. comienzan / ocho
4. Siempre estudio por la noche.
5. Aprendo mucho.

C. (5 points) ● ★
1. Vuelvo a la casa a las siete.
2. Primero me lavo las manos.
3. Luego como un poco.
4. Por último, me acuesto.
5. Me gusta dormir.

D. (10 optional points) ○
1. (queso) *(model)*
2. (garaje) *(model)*
3. (que)
4. (techo)
5. (cierras)
6. (pequeña)
7. (aquí)
8. (cena)
9. (quitarse)
10. (querido)
11. (guisantes)
12. (guitarra)

(Test masters 127–135)

Total points: 50 / Total extra credit points: 10 / Total optional points: 10

Section 1

(15 points)

A. (5 points) ○
1. cocinero / comedor *(model)*
2. directora / oficina
3. enfermera / enfermería
4. bibliotecario / biblioteca
5. maestra / salón de clase
6. conserje / pasillo

B. (5 points) ◐
1. director *(model)*
2. enfermera
3. cocinero
4. maestra
5. bibliotecaria
6. conserje

C. (5 points) ◐
1. salida *(model)*
2. fuente de agua
3. subir
4. auditorio
5. entrada
6. bajar

Section 2

(20 points; 5 points extra credit)

A. (7 points) ◐
1. sé
2. sabe
3. sabemos
4. sabes
5. saben
6. sabemos
7. sabe

B. (5 points) ◐
1. Nunca
2. Nadie
3. nada
4. bajar
5. salida

C. (8 points) ◐
1. sí
2. sí
3. no
4. sí
5. sí
6. sí
7. no
8. no

D. (5 points) ● ★

Paloma es muy <u>alta</u>.
¿Es <u>alta</u> su hermana?
Sí, Paloma y su hermana son
<u>altas</u>, pero su papá, es más <u>alto</u>
que ellas.
Todos son muy <u>altos</u>.

Section 3

(15 points; 5 points extra credit)

A. (5 points) ◐
1. Falso
2. Cierto
3. Falso
4. Cierto
5. Cierto

B. (10 points) ◐
1. trabaja / escuela
2. Qué / él
3. Sabe / todo
4. ¿Es el director?
5. No, es el conserje.

C. (5 points) ● ★
1. Rosa es la más inteligente de todas.
2. ¿Es más inteligente que Ana?
3. Sí, mucho más inteligente.
4. ¿Cómo lo sabes?
5. ¡Es mi hermana!

D. (10 optional points) ○
1. sí (gana) *(model)*
2. no (cama) *(model)*
3. sí (regalo)
4. no (flamenco)
5. sí (agosto)
6. no (cuarto)
7. no (cosa)
8. sí (figura)
9. sí (galón)
10. no (calor)
11. sí (goma)
12. sí (gusto)

(Test masters 136–142)

Total points: 50 / Total optional points: 10

Section 1
(15 points)

A. (5 points)
1. b (Hay un ropero en mi dormitorio.) *(model)*
2. e (Tenemos una batidora eléctrica.)
3. a (El buzón está delante de la casa.)
4. c (La lámpara es nueva.)
5. f (El abrelatas está en la cocina.)
6. d (Es un cuchillo.)

B. (5 points)
1. zanahorias *(model)*
2. huevos
3. pan
4. toronja
5. pone
6. regar

C. (5 points)
1. cabeza *(model)*
2. nada
3. pequeña
4. baja
5. vestido
6. ceja

Section 2
(20 points)

A. (5 points)
1. les
2. mí
3. sus
4. se
5. ellos

B. (15 points)
1. prueba
2. puede
3. piensan
4. te cepillas
5. sé
6. quieren
7. pone
8. tiene
9. usan
10. abrimos
11. están
12. son
13. almuerzan
14. duelen
15. quedan

Section 3
(15 points)

A. (5 points)
1. c (Sonia está *bien*.)
2. a (Jaime piensa *nadar*.)
3. b (Los padres de Sonia *no están*.)
4. c (José es el *hermanito*).
5. c (José sabe *comer*.)

B. (10 points)
1. comienzas / estudiar
2. Comienzo / nueve
3. ¿Te gusta estudiar tarde?
4. Claro que sí.
5. A mí no.

C. (10 optional points)
1. m<u>e</u>s *(model)*
2. <u>s</u>ala *(model)*
3. a<u>h</u>ora
4. h<u>i</u>jo
5. e<u>n</u>ero
6. a<u>b</u>ajo
7. niñ<u>o</u>
8. <u>q</u>uerido
9. cere<u>z</u>a
10. <u>r</u>ubia
11. <u>c</u>errar
12. do<u>ñ</u>a

TeaCHeR'S ReSOURCE CHARTS

Blackline Masters

¿QUÉ TAL? STUDENT PROGRESS CHART

Student's Name _____   Grade _____

Vocabulary Sections (Section 1)

Test	Points	Points Earned	Comments	Date
Placement	15			
Unidad 1	15			
Unidad 2	15			
Unidad 3	15			
Repaso: Unidades 1–3	10			
Unidad 4	15			
Unidad 5	15			
Unidad 6	15			
Repaso: Unidades 4–6	10			
Mid-Year	15			
Unidad 7	15			
Unidad 8	15			
Unidad 9	15			
Repaso: Unidades 7–9	10			
Unidad 10	15			
Unidad 11	15			
Unidad 12	15			
End-of-Year	15			
Total	**240**			

¿QUÉ TAL? STUDENT PROGRESS CHART

Student's Name _____ Grade _____

Structure Sections (Section 2)

Test	Points*	Points Earned	Comments	Date
Placement	20			
Unidad 1	20 (5)			
Unidad 2	20 (5)			
Unidad 3	20 (5)			
Repaso: Unidades 1–3	15			
Unidad 4	20 (5)			
Unidad 5	20 (5)			
Unidad 6	20 (5)			
Repaso: Unidades 4–6	15			
Mid-Year	20			
Unidad 7	20 (5)			
Unidad 8	20 (5)			
Unidad 9	20 (5)			
Repaso: Unidades 7–9	15			
Unidad 10	20 (5)			
Unidad 11	20 (5)			
Unidad 12	20 (5)			
End-of-Year	20			
Total	**325 (60)**			

* Numbers in parentheses represent extra-credit points.

¿QUÉ TAL? STUDENT PROGRESS CHART

Student's Name _____   Grade _____

Oral Sections (Section 3)

Test	Points*	Points Earned	Comments	Date
Placement	25			
Unidad 1	15 (5)			
Unidad 2	15 (5)			
Unidad 3	15 (5)			
Repaso: Unidades 1–3	15			
Unidad 4	15 (5)			
Unidad 5	15 (5)			
Unidad 6	15 (5)			
Repaso: Unidades 4–6	15			
Mid-Year	15			
Unidad 7	15 (5)			
Unidad 8	15 (5)			
Unidad 9	15 (5)			
Repaso: Unidades 7–9	15			
Unidad 10	15 (5)			
Unidad 11	15 (5)			
Unidad 12	15 (5)			
End-of-Year	15			
Total	255 (60)			

* Numbers in parentheses represent extra-credit points.

¿QUÉ TAL? COMPOSITE SCORE CHART

Student's Name _____ Grade _____

Test	Section	Subscores	Total Score	Date
Placement	Section 1	_____		_____
	Section 2	_____		_____
	Section 3	_____		_____
	Speaking	_____		_____
			_____	
Unidad **1**	Section 1	_____		_____
	Section 2	_____		_____
	Section 3	_____		_____
			_____	
Unidad **2**	Section 1	_____		_____
	Section 2	_____		_____
	Section 3	_____		_____
			_____	
Unidad **3**	Section 1	_____		_____
	Section 2	_____		_____
	Section 3	_____		_____
			_____	

¿QUÉ TAL? COMPOSITE SCORE CHART

Student's Name _____ Grade _____

Test	Section	Subscores	Total Score	Date
Repaso: Unidades 1–3	Section 1	_____		_____
	Section 2	_____		_____
	Section 3	_____		_____
			_____	
Unidad **4**	Section 1	_____		_____
	Section 2	_____		_____
	Section 3	_____		_____
			_____	
Unidad **5**	Section 1	_____		_____
	Section 2	_____		_____
	Section 3	_____		_____
			_____	
Unidad **6**	Section 1	_____		_____
	Section 2	_____		_____
	Section 3	_____		_____
			_____	
Repaso: Unidades 4–6	Section 1	_____		_____
	Section 2	_____		_____
	Section 3	_____		_____
			_____	

¿QUÉ TAL? COMPOSITE SCORE CHART

Student's Name _____ Grade _____

Test	Section	Subscores	Total Score	Date
Mid-Year	Section 1	_____		_____
	Section 2	_____		_____
	Section 3	_____		_____
			_____	
Unidad **7**	Section 1	_____		_____
	Section 2	_____		_____
	Section 3	_____		_____
			_____	
Unidad **8**	Section 1	_____		_____
	Section 2	_____		_____
	Section 3	_____		_____
			_____	
Unidad **9**	Section 1	_____		_____
	Section 2	_____		_____
	Section 3	_____		_____
			_____	
Repaso: Unidades 7–9	Section 1	_____		_____
	Section 2	_____		_____
	Section 3	_____		_____
			_____	

¿QUÉ TAL? COMPOSITE SCORE CHART

Student's Name _____   Grade _____

Test	Section	Subscores	Total Score	Date
Unidad **10**	Section 1	_____		_____
	Section 2	_____		_____
	Section 3	_____		_____
			_____	
Unidad **11**	Section 1	_____		_____
	Section 2	_____		_____
	Section 3	_____		_____
			_____	
Unidad **12**	Section 1	_____		_____
	Section 2	_____		_____
	Section 3	_____		_____
			_____	
End-of-Year	Section 1	_____		_____
	Section 2	_____		_____
	Section 3	_____		_____
			_____	

STUDENT TESTS

Blackline Masters

Nombre _____

Section 1

A. Read the sentences in the list below. Then look at the pictures. On the answer blank under each picture, write the letter of the sentence that matches the picture. The first one has been done for you.

a. Es mi ropero.
b. Son unas medias.
c. Un cuarto de baño está cerca.

d. Ella toca la nariz.
e. El lavaplatos es nuevo.
f. Luis plancha la ropa.

1.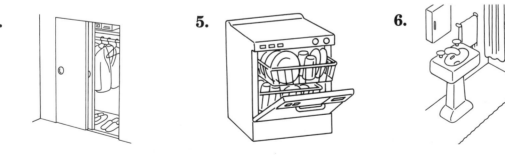

b

2.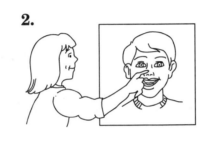

_____

3.

_____

4.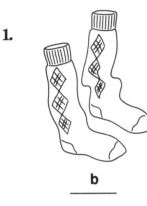

_____

5.

_____

6.

_____

Nombre _____

B. First, look at the picture. Then choose a word from the list that completes each sentence. Write the word on the answer blank. The first one has been done for you.

fritos	nadie	sandía
leche	pan	zanahorias

1.

Me gusta el ____**pan**____ .

2.

No quiero _____ .

3.

Vamos a comer huevos _____ .

4.

La _____ es fantástica.

5.

Hay un vaso de _____ .

6.

No hay _____ en el pasillo.

Nombre _____

c. Look at each picture. Then, on the answer blank, write the word that completes the sentence next to the picture. The first one has been done for you.

1.

El muchacho tiene que ser muy _____**fuerte**_____ .

2.

Es una _____ nueva.

3.

Le duelen los _____ .

➡

Nombre _____

Part **C**, *continued.*

_____

4.

La Sra. Chávez es _____ .

5.

Mi hermana es una muchacha _____ .

6.

Pedro se _____ la ropa.

Nombre _____

Section 2

A. Complete these sentences, using words from the list below. Follow the model.

ellas	se	ti
les	su	tus

M Elvira es más bonita que _____**su**_____ mamá.

1. A mis primos _____ gusta bailar.

2. ¿A _____ no te gustan los perros?

3. _____ hermanas son muy bonitas.

4. Jorge _____ levanta a las siete en punto.

5. Ana y Luisa son amigas; _____ siempre estudian.

B. Complete the sentences below. Write the correct form of the verb in parentheses. Follow the model.

M Carla _____**come**_____ bien.
(comer)

1. Pedro _____ cantar.
(poder)

2. Los muchachos _____ sus chaquetas nuevas.
(llevar)

Nombre _____

Part **B**, *continued.*

---

3. Los secretarios _____ a trabajar temprano.
(comenzar)

4. Tú _____ primero.
(peinarse)

5. Yo _____ hablar español.
(saber)

6. ¿Tú y Eduardo _____ estudiar?
(querer)

7. Beatriz siempre _____ la comida.
(traer)

8. ¿Usted _____ de nadar?
(acabar)

9. Ellas _____ a veces.
(cocinar)

10. Nosotras no _____ aquí.
(vivir)

11. ¿ _____ felices ustedes?
(estar)

12. Ellos _____ hermanos.
(ser)

13. ¿Por qué te _____ la cabeza?
(doler)

14. Le _____ muy bien las botas.
(quedar)

15. Nosotras siempre _____ la puerta.
(cerrar)

Nombre _____

Section 3

A. Listen to this conversation between Pablo and his father. Then you will hear five multiple-choice statements about their conversation. Circle the letter of the phrase that best completes each statement.

1. a   b   c   4. a   b   c

2. a   b   c   5. a   b   c

3. a   b   c

B. Dictado. Listen carefully to these sentences. You will hear each sentence twice. Write the missing words on the answer blanks.

1. Mi tía es _____ de una _____ .

2. Hoy _____ con _____ .

3. _____

4. _____

5. _____

C. This is a speaking test. Listen to your teacher's instructions.

PLACEMENT TEST

Nombre _____

D. Listen carefully to these twelve words. You will hear each word twice. Complete each word by writing a vowel or consonant letter on the answer blank. The first two have been done for you.

1. m __**e**__ sa

2. __**s**__ al

3. _____ ueves

4. h _____ ja

5. _____ evar

6. po _____ o

7. n _____ che

8. _____ ueso

9. s _____ cia

10. _____ ubio

11. _____ erca

12. _____ uerra

Nombre _____

Section 1

A. First look at the names of the parts of the body in the list. Then write the letter for each word on the correct answer blank in the picture below. The first one has been done for you.

a. la boca	**e.** el codo	**i.** la pierna
b. el brazo	**f.** los dedos	**j.** el pie
c. la cabeza	**g.** la mano	**k.** la rodilla
d. la cintura	**h.** el pelo	

1. h
2. ____
3. ____
4. ____
5. ____
6. ____
7. ____
8. ____
9. ____
10. ____
11. ____

Nombre _____

B. Look at the picture below with number labels. Then, on the answer blanks, write the names of the parts of the face. The first one has been done for you.

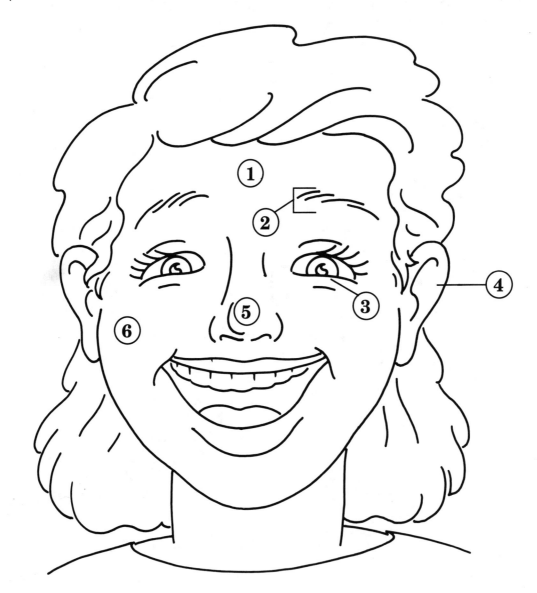

1. _____ **la frente** _____   4. _____

2. _____   5. _____

3. _____   6. _____

Nombre _____

Section 2

A. Complete each sentence below by circling **duele** or **duelen**.

[M] Me ((duele) , duelen) el ojo.

1. Me (duele , duelen) las piernas.

2. ¿Te (duele , duelen) el hombro?

3. Le (duele , duelen) las manos.

4. ¿Te (duele , duelen) los tobillos?

5. Me (duele , duelen) la lengua.

6. Le (duele , duelen) la rodilla.

7. ¿Te (duele , duelen) el brazo?

8. Me (duele , duelen) los pies.

9. Le (duele , duelen) la nariz.

10. Me (duele , duelen) los ojos.

Nombre _____

B. **¡Ojo!** Complete this paragraph that tells about parts of the body. Write **el, los, la,** or **las** on each answer blank. The first one has been done for you.

En ____la____ cabeza está _____ pelo. En _____ frente

están _____ cejas. _____ ojos y _____ nariz están

en _____ cara. _____ boca tiene _____ labios,

_____ dientes y _____ lengua.

★**C.** For extra credit, draw a line from the beginning to the end of each sentence. Be careful! A sentence may have more than one ending. The first one has been started for you.

a. ¿Qué le duele   a él?

                                       a ella?

b. ¿Qué te duele   a ti?

                                       a Rita?

c. ¿Qué me duele   a mí?

                                       a usted?

Nombre _____

Section 3

A. Listen to the conversation between Víctor and his **mamá**. Then you will hear five multiple-choice statements about their conversation. You will hear each statement twice. Circle the letter of the phrase that best completes each statement.

1. a   b   c   4. a   b   c

2. a   b   c   5. a   b   c

3. a   b   c

B. **Dictado.** Listen and then write the missing words. You will hear each sentence twice.

PAPÁ: ¿ _____ te duele, Carlitos?

CARLITOS: Me duele _____ .

PAPÁ: ¿ _____ y _____ te duele?

CARLITOS: Me duele _____ los _____

a las _____ de la _____

porque tengo clase de _____ .

UNIDAD 1 / EXAMEN

Nombre _____

★ **C.** Now try writing these sentences for extra credit. You will hear each sentence twice.

1. _____

2. _____

3. _____

4. _____

5. _____

D. Listen carefully to these twelve words. You will hear each word twice. Complete each word by writing **n** or **ñ** on the answer blank. The first two have been done for you.

1. bue __n__ o

2. a __ñ__ o

3. pu ____ to

4. sue ____ o

5. ni ____ o

6. ma ____ o

7. ____ ietos

8. espa ____ ol

9. i ____ glés

10. ci ____ tura

11. do ____ a

12. ju ____ io

Nombre _____

A. It's time for a shopping spree! First look at the picture. Then choose a phrase from the list to complete the sentence and to tell what you are going to buy.

una blusa	una chaqueta	una falda	un suéter
una camisa	un vestido	unos pantalones	

M Voy a comprar

un suéter.
_____
_____

1. Voy a comprar
_____
_____

2. Voy a comprar
_____
_____

3. Voy a comprar
_____
_____

4. Voy a comprar
_____
_____

5. Voy a comprar
_____
_____

6. Voy a comprar
_____
_____

Nombre _____

B. Now tell what you and your friends are going to wear. First, look at the picture. Then write the missing words that name the article of clothing in the picture.

M Voy a llevar

el sombrero.
_____

_____

1. Inés va a llevar

_____

_____

2. José va a llevar

_____

_____

3. Ana va a llevar

_____

_____

4. Ernesto va a llevar

_____

_____

5. Claudia va a llevar

_____

_____

6. Carlos va a llevar

_____

_____

Nombre _____

C. The T-shirts below come in three sizes only. Write **pequeña, grande,** or **mediana** under each T-shirt.

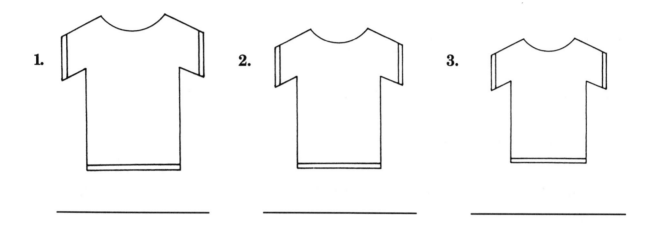

1. _____   2. _____   3. _____

Nombre _____

Section 2

A. Tell a friend how her clothes look. Complete each sentence by writing
queda or **quedan** on the answer blank.

M El suéter te _____**queda**_____ grande.

1. La blusa te _____ bien.

2. Los pantalones te _____ largos.

3. Los zapatos te _____ grandes.

4. El sombrero te _____ bien.

5. El abrigo te _____ corto.

6. Las medias te _____ mal.

Nombre _____

B. Circle the letter for the word that best completes each of the sentences.

M El sombrero te queda...

    a.   pequeños.

    b.   pequeña.

    (c.) pequeño.

1. El suéter te queda...

    a.   corta.

    b.   corto.

    c.   cortos.

2. La camisa es...

    a.   bonita.

    b.   bonito.

    c.   bonitos.

3. Las botas son...

    a.   feos.

    b.   feas.

    c.   fea.

4. Los zapatos te quedan...

    a.   pequeña.

    b.   pequeño.

    c.   pequeños.

5. La bata te queda...

    a.   corta.

    b.   corto.

    c.   cortas.

6. El pijama te queda...

    a.   largos.

    b.   larga.

    c.   largo.

Nombre _____

C. Tell who owns what! Use the words below to complete the sentences. The first one has been done for you.

| del | de él | de los | de la | de las |

1. El libro es ____del____ profesor.

2. El pupitre es _____ alumna.

3. ¿Son de Alberto los zapatos? Sí, son _____ .

4. La camisa es _____ hombre.

5. La blusas son _____ tías.

6. Las medias son _____ hijos.

7. Los mapas son _____ abuela.

8. ¿Es de Juan la chaqueta? Sí, es _____ .

9. El sombrero es _____ alumno.

★D. For extra credit, complete the conversation below. Use the words from the list. The first one has been done for you.

| soy | son | llevo | lleva |
| es | voy | llevas | llevar |

1. P: ¿Qué ropa ____llevas____ en enero?

   R: Yo _____ un abrigo.

2. P: ¿Cómo _____ el abrigo?

   R: Es grande.

3. P: ¿De quién _____ las botas?

   R: Son de mi hermana. Mañana yo _____ a _____ sus botas.

Nombre _____

Section 3

A. Listen to the conversation between señora Oteo and a salesclerk. Then you will hear five statements about their conversation. You will hear each statement twice. Circle **CIERTO** if the statement is true. Circle **FALSO** if it is false.

1. CIERTO   FALSO

2. CIERTO   FALSO

3. CIERTO   FALSO

4. CIERTO   FALSO

5. CIERTO   FALSO

B. Dictado. Listen and write the missing words. You will hear each sentence twice.

RAÚL: ¿Dónde está mi ropa de _____?

MAMÁ: No _____ .

RAÚL: ¿De quién es la _____?

Es _____ .

MAMÁ: Es de tu hermano Carlos. Te queda _____ .

RAÚL: ¿De quién es el _____?

MAMÁ: Es de tu _____ Pedro.

RAÚL: ¿Y los _____? ¡Son _____!

MAMÁ: Son _____ zapatos nuevos para ir a la escuela.

Nombre _____

★ **C.** Now try writing these sentences for extra credit. You will hear each sentence twice.

1. _____

2. _____

3. _____

4. _____

5. _____

D. Listen carefully to the following words. You will hear each word twice. If a word has an **h** in it, circle **sí**. If it does not, circle **no**. The first two have been done for you.

1. (sí) no		5. sí no		9. sí no
2. sí (no)		6. sí no		10. sí no
3. sí no		7. sí no		11. sí no
4. sí no		8. sí no		12. sí no

Nombre _____

Section 1

A. Describe these people. First, look at the picture. Then choose a word from the list to complete the sentence under the picture. The first one has been done for you.

alto	baja	delgado	gruesa
alta	débil	fuerte	grueso

1.

Luis es

delgado

_____ .

2.

Pablo es

_____ .

3.

Ana es

_____ .

4.

Clara es

_____ .

5.

Pedro es

_____ .

6.

Eduardo es

_____ .

Nombre _____

B. Imagine that these students are your classmates. First, look at the picture. Then complete the sentence by writing a word that describes each student's personality. The first one has been done for you.

1.

Jaime es _____**inteligente**_____ .

2.

María es _____ .

3.

Consuelo es _____ .

4.

Paco es _____ .

5.

Mónica es _____ .

6.

Fernando es _____ .

Nombre _____

Part **B**, *continued.*

7.

8.

Raúl es _____ .

Donaldo es _____ .

C. Look at the picture. Then write a word on the answer blank to tell whether the student's hair is straight, curly, or wavy.

1.

Ana tiene el pelo _____ .

2.

Paco tiene el pelo _____ .

3.

Rebeca tiene el pelo _____ .

Nombre _____

Section 2

A. Imagine that you are telling a teacher about yourself and your family. Complete the conversation below by writing **soy, eres, es,** or **son** on the answer blanks. The first one has been done for you.

1. Mi papá _____**es**_____ alto.

2. Mi mamá _____ delgada.

3. ¿Tú _____ delgado?

4. Sí, y mi papá _____ muy delgado.

5. ¿Cómo _____ tus hermanas?

6. Ellas _____ atléticas y muy bonitas.

7. ¿Tú _____ fuerte o débil?

8. Yo _____ muy fuerte.

9. Usted _____ muy atlético.

Nombre _____

B.   Look at the picture. Then choose words from the list to complete the sentences that compare what you see in each picture.

alta	grande	más
delgada	largo	menos

M

Mi abrigo es _____**más**_____

_____**largo**_____ que tu abrigo.

Tu abrigo es _____**menos**_____

_____**largo**_____ que mi abrigo.

mi abrigo   tu abrigo

1.

Lupe es _____ _____
que Pilar.

Pilar es _____ _____
que Lupe.

Lupe   Pilar

2.

Tu gato es _____ _____
que mi gato.

Mi gato es _____ _____
que tu gato.

mi gato   tu gato

3.

Ema es _____ _____
que Anita.

Anita es _____ _____
que Ema.

Anita   Ema

Nombre _____

★ **C.** Beatriz has something good to say about everyone, including herself! Complete each of her comments by writing **soy, eres, es,** or **son** on the answer blanks.

[M] ¡Qué generoso ____**es**____ usted!

1. ¡Qué delgada _____ tú!

2. ¡Qué inteligentes _____ Luis y Anita!

3. ¡Qué atlético _____ Juan!

4. ¡Qué simpáticos _____ tus abuelitos!

5. ¡Qué popular _____ yo!

Nombre _____

Section 3

A. Listen to the conversation between Estela and Alicia. Then you will hear five multiple-choice statements about their conversation. You will hear each statement twice. Circle the letter of the word that best completes each statement.

1.   a   b   c

2.   a   b   c

3.   a   b   c

4.   a   b   c

5.   a   b   c

B. **Dictado.** Listen carefully and write the missing words. You will hear each sentence twice.

1. ¿De _____ _____ son tus ojos?

2. _____ los ojos _____ .

3. ¿_____ son los ojos de tu _____ ?

4. Son más _____ que _____ ojos.

5. _____ tiene los ojos _____ .

Nombre _____

★ **C.** Now try writing these sentences for extra credit. You will hear each
sentence twice.

1. _____

2. _____

3. _____

4. _____

5. _____

D. Listen carefully to the following words. You will hear each word twice.
Complete each word by writing **b** or **v** on the answer blank. The first four
have been done for you.

1. __b__ ajo

2. a __b__ ajo

3. __v__ erano

4. prima __v__ era

5. _____ erdad

6. a _____ rigo

7. _____ lusa

8. no _____ iembre

9. a _____ uela

10. _____ as

11. ca _____ eza

12. _____ otas

13. di _____ ertido

14. _____ einte

Nombre _____

Section 1

A. Read the words in the list. Then look at each picture below. On the answer blank, write the word that completes the sentence. The first one has been done for you.

popular	ceja	débil
espalda	feo	pantalones

1.

¿Quién toca la

ceja _____ ?

2.

Son los _____

de Sara .

3.

Juanito es un muchacho

_____ .

4.

Lucinda es una alumna

muy _____ .

5.

No me gusta el vestido.

Es _____ .

6.

A Pedro le duele la

_____ .

REPASO: UNIDADES 1–3 / EXAMEN

Nombre _____

B. Look at the picture. Then write a word on the answer blank to complete the sentence under the picture. The first one has been done for you.

1.

¿Por qué es ____**impaciente**____ David?

2.

Nado en mi traje de _____ .

3.

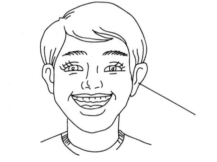

Es la _____ de Miguel.

4.

Son los _____ de Lisa.

5.

La _____ de Carlos es bonita.

6.

Beto tiene el pelo negro y _____ .

¿QUÉ TAL?

Nombre _____

Section 2

A. You and your friends are on a clothes shopping spree. Complete the sentences telling how the different items fit. Use **queda** or **quedan** and the word in parentheses.

M (grande) Me ___**quedan**___ ___**grandes**___ los zapatos.

1. (corto) Jorge, te _____ _____ la chaqueta.

2. (pequeño) A Mario le _____ _____ la camiseta.

3. (largo) A Susana le _____ _____ las dos faldas.

B. A lot of people at your school aren't feeling well today. Underline the words that complete each sentence below.

M Carmen, te duelen (el dedo, <u>los dedos</u>)?

1. A Pepe le duele (el ojo, los ojos).

2. A Nora le duele (el diente, los dientes).

3. Sra. Martínez, ¿a usted le duelen (la pierna, las piernas)?

4. ¡Qué cómico! ¡A Flora le duelen (la pestaña, las pestañas)!

Nombre _____

C. Ana and Pilar are arguing again! Complete Pilar's statements to make them the opposite of Ana's.

ANA: Celia es menos impaciente que Olga.

PILAR: No, Celia es ___**más**___ impaciente que Olga.

1. ANA: Jorge es más fuerte que Alberto.

   PILAR: No, Jorge es _____ fuerte que Alberto.

2. ANA Débora es más alta que Luis.

   PILAR: No, Débora es _____ alta que Luis.

3. ANA El vestido rojo es menos feo que el vestido azul.

   PILAR: No, el vestido rojo es _____ feo que el vestido azul.

4. ANA Yo soy más atlética que tú.

   PILAR: No, tú eres _____ atlética que yo.

5. ANA El pelo de Luz es menos lacio que el pelo de Marisol.

   PILAR: No, el pelo de Luz es _____ lacio que el pelo de Marisol.

Nombre _____

Section 3

A. Listen to the conversation between Liliana and Rosa. Then you will hear five statements about their conversation. You will hear each statement twice. Circle **CIERTO** if the statement is true. Circle **FALSO** if it is false.

1.   CIERTO   FALSO

2.   CIERTO   FALSO

3.   CIERTO   FALSO

4.   CIERTO   FALSO

5.   CIERTO   FALSO

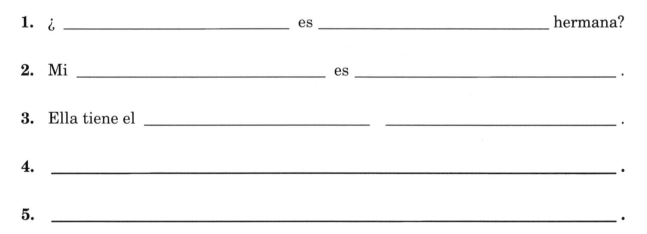

B.   **Dictado.** Listen carefully to these sentences. You will hear each sentence twice. Write the missing words on the answer blanks.

1. ¿ _____ es _____ hermana?

2. Mi _____ es _____ .

3. Ella tiene el _____ _____ .

4. _____ .

5. _____ .

Nombre _____

C. Listen carefully to these twelve words. You will hear each word twice. Complete each word by writing a vowel or a consonant on the answer blank. The first two have been done for you.

1. __u__ na

2. __h__ umano

3. espa ____ ol

4. ____ ijo

5. ____ año

6. ____ entana

7. ____ istoria

8. a ____ o

9. ____ egro

10. do ____ a

11. ____ oca

12. ____ estido

Nombre _____

Section 1

A. ¿Cómo es la casa? Describe the house. First, read the words in the list. (You will not use every word!) Then look at the picture below. On each answer blank, write the letter of the words that identify that part of the house. The first one has been done for you.

a. el balcón	**c.** la chimenea	**e.** el garaje	**g.** el patio
b. el buzón	**d.** las escaleras	**f.** el jardín	**h.** el techo

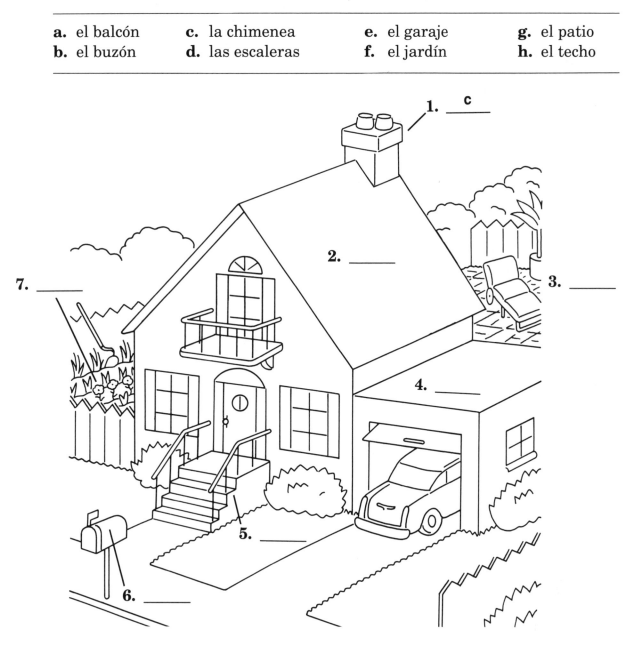

1. __c__

2. ____

3. ____

4. ____

5. ____

6. ____

7. ____

Nombre _____

B. **¿Cómo es el apartamento?** Describe the apartment. First look at the picture. Then choose a word from the list below to complete the sentence beside the picture. Write the word on the answer blank. Follow the model.

cocina	cuarto de baño	dormitorio	sótano
comedor	despacho	sala	

M

Hay _____ **sótano** _____ .

1.

Hay _____ .

2.

Hay _____ .

3.

Hay _____ .

Nombre _____

Part **B**, continued.

_____

4.

Tiene _____ .

5.

Tiene _____ .

6.

Tiene _____ .

C. Inside or outside? Complete each sentence below. On each answer blank, write the word that tells whether something is inside or outside the house.

1. La sala está _____ de la casa.

2. El balcón está _____ de la casa.

3. El despacho está _____ de la casa.

Nombre _____

Section 2

A. Underline the word that completes each sentence below.

M Celia ——— en el balcón.
(estoy / estás / <u>está</u>)

1. Pacha y Ramón ——— en la sala.
(está / estamos / están)

2. Óscar ——— en el sótano.
(estoy / estás / está)

3. ¿Tú ——— en la cocina?
(estoy / estás / está)

4. ¿Dónde estás? Yo ——— fuera de la casa.
(estoy / estás / está)

5. Ahora tú ——— dentro de la casa.
(estoy / estás / está)

6. Claudio y Alba ——— en el patio.
(está / estamos / están)

7. Luz y yo ——— en las escaleras.
(estoy / estamos / están)

Nombre _____

B. Look at the picture. Then choose the word from the list below that tells who is doing the action. The first one has been done for you.

yo	él	usted	nosotras	ellas
tú	ella	nosotros	ellos	ustedes

1.

yo

2.

_____

3.

_____

4.

_____

5.

_____

6.

_____

Nombre _____

C. Imagine that you are talking to a friend about the people named below. On the answer blank, write the word you would use to talk about them.

M Arturo, Claudia y yo = _____ nosotros _____

1. Elena y Rubén = _____

2. Elsa, Jaime y yo = _____

3. Isabel y Marta = _____

4. Jorge y Hugo = _____

5. Sara y tú = _____

6. la señora Casas y Ana = _____

7. Mateo y usted = _____

8. la señora López y yo (una muchacha) = _____

★ **D.** Now, for extra credit, describe your house. Complete each sentence by writing **dentro de** or **fuera de** on the answer blank.

M La cocina está _____ dentro de _____ la casa.

1. El techo está _____ la casa.

2. El sótano está _____ la casa.

3. La sala está _____ la casa.

4. El balcón está _____ la casa.

5. El despacho está _____ la casa.

Nombre _____

Section 3

A. Listen to the conversation between Pacha and Celia. Then you will hear five statements about their conversation. You will hear each statement twice. Circle **CIERTO** if the statement is true. Circle **FALSO** if it is false.

1.   CIERTO   FALSO

2.   CIERTO   FALSO

3.   CIERTO   FALSO

4.   CIERTO   FALSO

5.   CIERTO   FALSO

B.   Dictado. Listen carefully to these sentences. You will hear each sentence twice. Write the missing words on the answer blanks.

1. ¿ _____ es tu _____ ?

2. Es _____   _____ .

3. _____ seis _____ .

4. _____

5. _____

Nombre _____

★ **C.** Now try writing these sentences for extra credit. You will hear each sentence twice.

1. _____

2. _____

3. _____

4. _____

5. _____

D. Listen carefully to these twelve words. You will hear each word twice. Complete each word by writing **a, e, i, o,** or **u** on the answer blank. The first two have been done for you.

1. p __a__ tio

2. b __u__ zón

3. sót _____ no

4. coc _____ na

5. d _____ rmitorio

6. d _____ ntro

7. _____ stedes

8. balcon _____ s

9. despach _____

10. _____ na

11. g _____ raje

12. ch _____ menea

Section 1

A. Tell what is in the living room. First, look at the picture. Then choose a sentence that tells about the picture. Write the letter of the sentence on the answer blank. The first one has been done for you.

---

a. Hay cortinas.
b. Hay una lámpara.
c. Hay una alfombra en el piso.

d. Hay un retrato de la familia.
e. Hay un sofá grande.
f. Hay un televisor.

---

1. 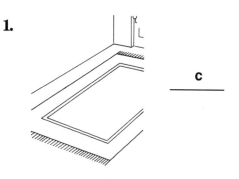   c

2.  ____

3.  ____

4.  ____

5. 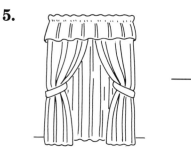 ____

6.  ____

Nombre _____

B.   ¿Dónde está? Look at the picture. Then underline the words that complete the sentence about the picture. The first one has been done for you.

1.

Diego está (en un sillón, en un sofá,

en un ropero).

2.

Rita está lejos (de la alfombra,

del sillón, de la lámpara).

3.

Sara está detrás (de la videocasetera,

del sofá, del tocador).

Nombre _____

Part **B**, *continued.*

4.

Luis está cerca (de la cama, del estante,

del equipo de sonido).

5.

Tilín está lejos (de la mesita de noche,

del retrato, del equipo de sonido).

6.

Tilín está delante (del estante,

de la almohada, del espejo).

Nombre _____

C. **¿Qué tienes en tu dormitorio?** Look at the picture. Then write a word on the answer blank to tell what the picture shows. The first one has been done for you.

1.

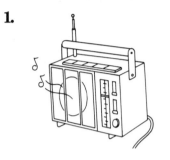

Hay un ___radio___ .

2.

Hay una _____ .

3.

Hay una _____ .

4.

Hay un _____ .

5.

Hay un _____ .

6.

Hay un _____ .

Nombre _____

Section 2

A. The first statement in each pair of sentences is wrong. You can correct it. Find the phrase below that means the opposite of the underlined phrase in the first sentence. Write it on the answer blank in the second sentence.

cerca de	delante de	detrás de	lejos de
cerca del	delante del	detrás del	lejos del

M El radio está <u>cerca del</u> televisor.

No, el radio está _____**lejos del**_____ televisor.

M La casa está <u>lejos de</u> la escuela.

No, la casa está _____**cerca de**_____ la escuela.

1. El buzón está <u>detrás</u> de la casa.

No, el buzón está _____ la casa.

2. El patio está <u>delante de</u> la casa.

No, el patio está _____ la casa.

3. La cocina está <u>lejos del</u> comedor.

No, la cocina está _____ comedor.

Nombre _____

Part **A**, *continued.*

---

4. El pupitre está <u>cerca de</u> la pizarra.

No, el pupitre está _____ la pizarra.

5. El teléfono está <u>detrás</u> de la cortina.

No, el teléfono está _____ la cortina.

6. La profesora vive <u>cerca de</u> la escuela.

No, la profesora vive _____ la escuela.

7. La silla está <u>delante del</u> escritorio.

No, la silla está _____ escritorio.

8. El apartamento está <u>cerca del</u> cine.

No, el apartamento está _____ cine.

Nombre _____

B.   ¡Hay dos! Complete the sentences below to show that there are more than one of each underlined item. Watch for exceptions to the rules!

M   El <u>espejo</u> es <u>alto.</u>

Los ____**espejos**____ son ____**altos**____ .

M   El <u>pez</u> es <u>pequeño.</u>

Los ____**peces**____ son ____**pequeños**____ .

1. La <u>alumna</u> es <u>bonita.</u>

Las _____ son _____ .

2. El <u>cartel</u> es <u>feo.</u>

Los _____ son _____ .

3. La <u>mano</u> de Ana es <u>delgada.</u>

Las _____ de Ana son _____ .

4. El <u>lápiz</u> es <u>azul.</u>

Los _____ son _____ .

5. El <u>mapa</u> es <u>grande.</u>

Los _____ son _____ .

6. El <u>sofá</u> es <u>amarillo.</u>

Los _____ son _____ .

Nombre _____

★ **C.** Each sentence below describes more than one person or thing. Read the sentence. Then, on the answer blank, write the sentence again, changing it to tell about one person or thing. Read the model.

M Tengo tres carteles bonitos.

    Tengo un cartel bonito. _____

1. Los estantes son largos.

    _____

2. Los teléfonos azules están cerca de las paredes.

    _____

3. Hay dos tocadores altos.

    _____

4. Tres mujeres son simpáticas.

    _____

5. ¿Son grandes las manos?

    _____

Nombre _____

Section 3

A. Listen to the conversation between Esteban, Sr. Olvida, and Raquel. Then you will hear five multiple-choice statements about their conversation. You will hear each statement twice. Circle the letter of the phrase that best completes each statement.

1. a   b   c

2. a   b   c

3. a   b   c

4. a   b   c

5. a   b   c

B.   **Dictado.** Listen carefully to these sentences. You will hear each sentence twice. Write the missing words on the answer blanks.

1. ¿ _____ es la _____ ?

2. Es grande _____ tiene muchos _____ .

3. ¿ _____   _____ hay ?

4. _____

5. _____

Nombre _____

★ **C.** Now try writing these sentences for extra credit. You will hear each sentence twice.

1. _____

2. _____

3. _____

4. _____

5. _____

D. You will hear a number and a word. If the word has an **r** sound, circle the number. If the word does not have an **r** sound, do not circle the number. The first two have been done for you.

(1.) (cortina)	4.	7.	10.
2. (alta)	5.	8.	11.
3.	6.	9.	12.

Nombre _____

Section 1

A. Tell what items a cook needs in the kitchen. First, look at the picture. Then read the list to find the words that name the item. Write the letter of the words on the answer blank.

---

a. el abrelatas   **d.** el fregadero   **g.** el horno de microondas
b. la batidora eléctrica   **e.** la licuadora   **h.** el lavaplatos
c. la estufa   **f.** el horno   **i.** la bombilla

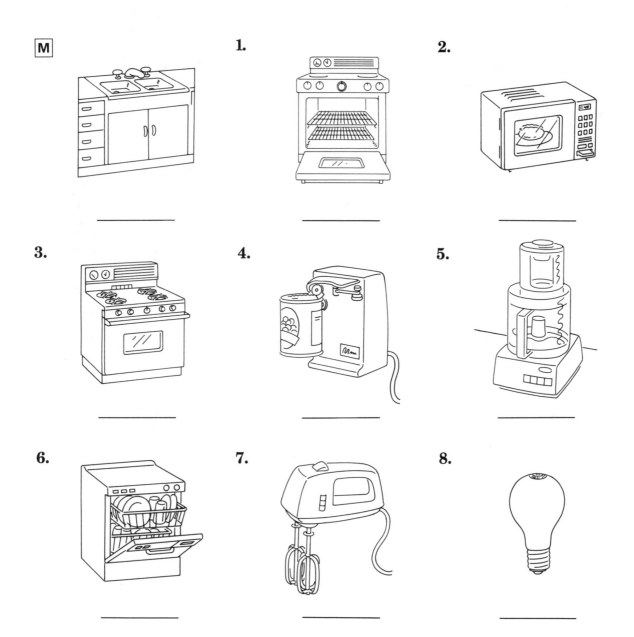

M.

1.

2.

_____

3.

4.

5.

_____

6.

7.

8.

_____

Nombre _____

B.   En la cocina. First look at the picture. Then complete the sentence by writing a word that names the thing in the picture. The first one has been done for you.

1.

Me gusta usar la **licuadora** _____ .

2.

Voy a abrir la _____ .

3.

Papá usa la batidora eléctrica y un

_____ .

4.

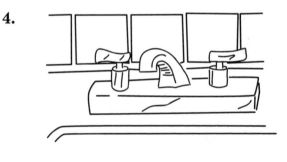

El _____ está cerca

del refrigerador.

Nombre _____

Part **B**, *continued.*

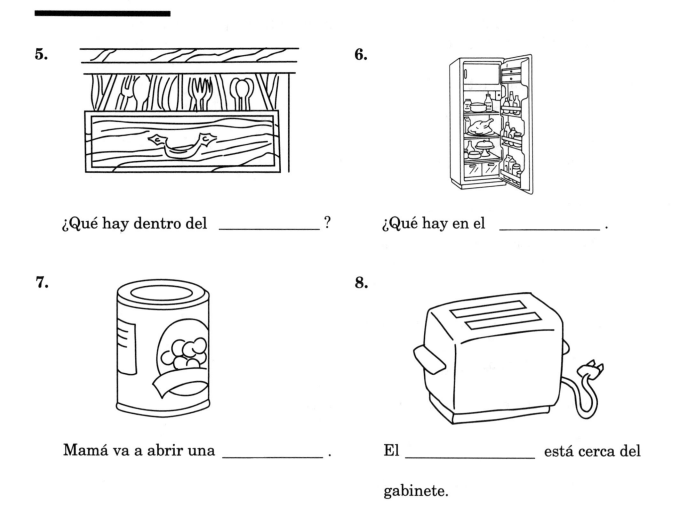

5.

¿Qué hay dentro del _____ ?

6.

¿Qué hay en el _____ .

7.

Mamá va a abrir una _____ .

8.

El _____ está cerca del gabinete.

Nombre _____

Section 2

A. Little David wants to know everything. Now he is questioning you.
Complete your answers to his questions.

M   DAVID: ¿Qué pintas?

      TÚ: _____**Pinto**_____ retratos.

1.   DAVID: ¿A qué hora comen ustedes?

      TÚ: _____ a las ocho de la noche.

2.   DAVID: ¿Cocina bien tu mamá?

      TÚ: Sí, _____ muy bien.

3.   DAVID: ¿Quién usa la batidora eléctrica?

      TÚ: Mi papá _____ la batidora.

4.   DAVID: ¿Qué usas más, el horno o la estufa?

      TÚ: _____ la estufa.

5.   DAVID: ¿Dónde aprendo yo a cocinar?

      TÚ: _____ en tu casa.

6.   DAVID: ¿Quién camina al cine?

      TÚ: Luis y Rita _____ al cine.

Nombre _____

Part **A**, continued.

---

7. DAVID: ¿Quién escribe muchas cartas?

   TÚ: Mi papá _____ muchas cartas.

8. DAVID: ¿Quién lee muchos libros?

   TÚ: Tus padres _____ muchos libros.

9. DAVID: ¿Quién abre la puerta?

   TÚ: Mi hermana _____ la puerta.

10. DAVID: ¿Quién mira la televisión?

    TÚ: Nosotros _____ la televisión.

B. Don Lucio knows something about everyone in the neighborhood. Learn what he knows by completing his comments. Use the correct form of each verb in parentheses.

M̄ Carla _____**mira**_____ la televisión a las once de la noche.
         (mirar)

1. Eva _____ en el sótano de su casa.
        (vivir)

2. Nora y Raúl _____ todos los días.
              (correr)

Nombre _____

Part **B**, *continued.*

━━━━━━━━━

3. Olga y Luis _____ todos los sábados.
(bailar)

4. Yo _____ a las seis de la mañana.
(caminar)

5. Tú y yo _____ muchas cartas.
(escribir)

6. Ricardo nunca _____ las ventanas.
(abrir)

7. Usted _____ casas.
(pintar)

8. Eduardo no _____ las matemáticas.
(comprender)

9. Nosotros no _____ mucho la computadora.
(usar)

10. Lola y Elena _____ mucho.
(comer)

Nombre _____

★ **C.** For extra credit, complete this note from Samuel to his computer teacher. On each answer blank write the correct form of the verb **usar.**

Estimado profesor:

En el salón de clase sólo hay dos computadoras. Por lo general,

los viernes a las cinco de la tarde, yo _____ la

computadora nueva. Juan y Marta también _____ la

computadora nueva los viernes por la tarde. A veces Juan, Marta y yo

_____ la vieja. ¿Hay posibilidad de usar yo la

computadora nueva mañana a las cinco de la tarde? Si mañana usted

y los alumnos _____ las computadoras, me voy y

_____ la computadora de un amigo.

Atentamente,

Samuel

Nombre _____

Section 3

A. Listen to the conversation between Iris and her father. Then you will hear five statements about their conversation. You will hear each statement twice. Circle **CIERTO** if the statement is true. Circle **FALSO** if it is false.

1. CIERTO   FALSO

2. CIERTO   FALSO

3. CIERTO   FALSO

4. CIERTO   FALSO

5. CIERTO   FALSO

B. Dictado. Listen carefully to these sentences. You will hear each sentence twice. Write the missing words on the answer blanks.

1. En _____ casa, ¿todos _____ ?

2. No, _____ no _____ .

3. ¿Usan el _____ de _____ ?

4. Sí, y _____ el _____ .

5. ¿Hay _____ _____ ?

Nombre _____

★ **C.** Now try writing these sentences for extra credit. You will hear each sentence twice.

1. _____

2. _____

3. _____

4. _____

5. _____

D. Listen carefully to these twelve words. You will hear each word twice. If you hear the consonant sound **erre** in a word, circle **sí**. If you do not hear the consonant sound **erre**, circle **no**. The first two have been done for you.

1.	(sí)	no	**5.**	sí	no	**9.**	sí	no
2.	sí	(no)	**6.**	sí	no	**10.**	sí	no
3.	sí	no	**7.**	sí	no	**11.**	sí	no
4.	sí	no	**8.**	sí	no	**12.**	sí	no

Nombre _____

Section 1

A. Read the words in the list. Then look at each picture below. On the answer blank, write the word that completes the sentence. The first one has been done for you.

cocina	estufa	enchufe
estante	garaje	piso

1.

El _____garaje_____ es nuevo.

2.

Hay libros en el _____.

3.

El _____ no tiene alfombra.

4.

La _____ es blanca.

5.

Hay una mesa en la _____.

6.

El _____ es importante.

¿QUÉ TAL?

Nombre _____

B. Look at the picture. Then write a word on the answer blank to complete the sentence under the picture. The first one has been done for you.

1.

Mi casa tiene

_____**comedor**_____ .

2.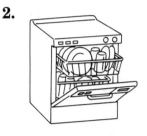

El _____ está

en la cocina.

3.

Es un _____

de mi familia.

4.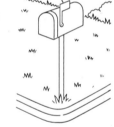

Recibo cartas en el

_____ .

5.

Uso mucho el

_____ .

6.

En el dormitorio hay un

_____ .

Nombre _____

Section 2

A. ¿Dónde está? Read the first sentence of each pair and look at the underlined phrase. Then find the phrase in the list that has the opposite meaning and write it on the answer blank.

cerca de	detrás de
delante de	fuera de
dentro de	lejos de

M La casa está <u>lejos de</u> la escuela.

La casa está _____**cerca de**_____ la escuela.

1. La muchacha está <u>dentro de</u> la casa.

La muchacha está _____ la casa.

2. El niño está <u>fuera de</u> su cuarto.

El niño está _____ su cuarto.

3. El garaje está <u>delante de</u> la casa.

El garaje está _____ la casa.

4. La silla está <u>detrás de</u> la mesa.

La silla está _____ la mesa.

Nombre _____

B. Complete the sentences below to show that there are more than one of each person or thing.

M La muchacha es bonita.

Las ___**muchachas**___ son ___**bonitas**___ .

1. El alumno es grande.

Los _____ son _____ .

2. La pared es alta.

Las _____ son _____ .

3. El mapa es pequeño.

Los _____ son _____ .

Nombre _____

C. Complete each sentence. Write the correct form of the verb in parentheses.

M Jaime _____**escribe**_____ la lección.
     (escribir)

1. ¿David? Él _____ en San Diego.
   (estar)

2. Nosotros _____ lejos de la casa.
   (estar)

3. Yo no _____ muy bien.
   (pintar)

4. Ellas _____ mucho.
   (leer)

5. ¿Dónde _____ ustedes?
   (vivir)

Nombre _____

Section 3

A. Listen to the conversation between Alma and Pedro. Then you will hear five multiple-choice statements about their conversation. Circle the letter of the phrase that best completes each statement.

1.   a   b   c

2.   a   b   c

3.   a   b   c

4.   a   b   c

5.   a   b   c

B. **Dictado.** Listen carefully to these sentences. You will hear each sentence twice. Write the missing words on the answer blanks.

1. En el _____ _____ en el patio.

2. El patio está _____ de la _____ .

3. A mi mamá le _____ _____ .

4. _____

5. _____

Nombre _____

C. Listen carefully to these twelve words. You will hear each word twice. Complete each word by writing a vowel or consonant letter on the answer blank. The first two have been done for you.

1. __e__ stán

2. __r__ opa

3. b _____ blioteca

4. t _____ abajo

5. pe _____ o

6. suci _____

7. vid _____

8. t _____ mar

9. m _____ jer

10. t _____ cho

11. _____ ío

12. alfomb _____ a

Section 1

A. Read the sentences below. Then look at the pictures. On the answer blank under each picture, write the letter of the sentence that matches the picture. The first one has been done for you.

a. Es el techo de la casa.
b. Hay un despacho.
c. Mi casa tiene sótano.

d. En el dormitorio hay un espejo.
e. Tenemos un televisor grande.
f. Es el sillón de mi papá.

1.

c
_____

2.

_____

3.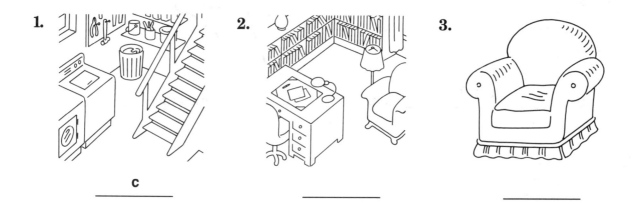

_____

4.

_____

5.

_____

6.

_____

Nombre _____

B. First, look at the picture. Then choose the word that completes the sentence under the picture. Write the word on the answer blank. The first one has been done for you.

| enchufe | estufa | ondulado | licuadora | gorra | dedos |

1.

Es una _____**estufa**_____ blanca.

2.

La mano tiene cinco _____ .

3.

Tenemos una _____ en la cocina.

4.

Hay un _____ .

5.

Voy a comprar una _____ .

6.

Ana   Lupe

Lupe tiene el pelo _____ .

Nombre _____

c. Look at each picture. Then, on the answer blank, write the word that completes the sentence under the picture. The first one has been done for you.

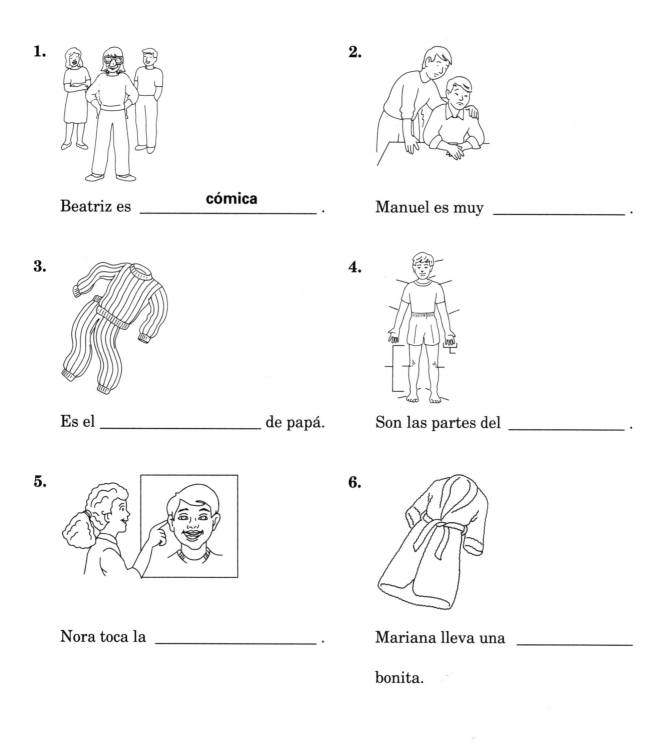

1.

Beatriz es _____ **cómica** _____ .

2.

Manuel es muy _____ .

3.

Es el _____ de papá.

4.

Son las partes del _____ .

5.

Nora toca la _____ .

6.

Mariana lleva una _____

bonita.

Mid-Year Test

Nombre _____

Section 2

A. Complete the sentences below. On the answer blank, write the correct form of each verb in parentheses.

M Sara estudia mucho. Ella ____**lee**____ todos los días.
(leer)

1. Enrique es atlético. Él _____ todas las mañanas.
(caminar)

2. Silvia y Luis son inteligentes. Ellos _____ rápido.
(aprender)

3. Elena es popular. Ella _____ muchas cartas.
(escribir)

4. Mamá y Rosita están contentas. Ellas _____ la televisión.
(mirar)

5. ¿ _____ usted lejos de la escuela?
(estar)

Nombre _____

Part **A**, *continued.*

_____

6. Nosotros _____ a las siete en punto.
(comer)

7. A Ernesto le _____ los tobillos.
(doler)

8. Te _____ muy bien los pantalones negros.
(quedar)

9. Nosotros _____ en el garaje.
(estar)

10. Ustedes _____ muchas cajas.
(abrir)

Mid-Year Test

Nombre _____

B. **¡Hay más!** Rewrite the sentences below to show that there are more than one of each person or thing. The first one has been done for you.

1. El niño es pequeño.

   Los niños son pequeños.
   _____

2. La señora es alta.

   _____

3. El sombrero es feo.

   _____

4. Tu pared es amarilla.

   _____

5. Su lápiz es rojo.

   _____

6. El mapa es grande.

   _____

¿QUÉ TAL?

Nombre _____

Section 3

A. Listen to the conversation between Teresa and Manuel. Then you will hear five multiple-choice statements about their conversation. Circle the letter of the phrase that best completes each statement.

1. a   b   c

2. a   b   c

3. a   b   c

4. a   b   c

5. a   b   c

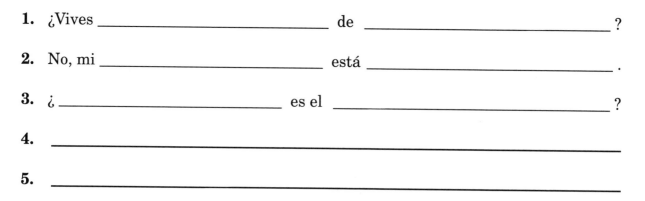

B. **Dictado.** Listen carefully to these sentences. You will hear each sentence twice. Write the missing words on the answer blanks.

1. ¿Vives _____ de _____ ?

2. No, mi _____ está _____ .

3. ¿ _____ es el _____ ?

4. _____

5. _____

Mid-Year Test

Nombre _____

C. Listen carefully to these twelve words. You will hear each word twice. Complete each word by writing a vowel or consonant letter on the answer blank. The first two have been done for you.

1. c __a__ si

2. ense__ñ__ a

3. _____ otel

4. m _____ sa

5. _____ aca

6. l _____ ro

7. l _____ gar

8. _____ acho

9. _____ ablar

10. p _____ ña

11. ci _____ e

12. tam _____ ién

Nombre _____

Section 1

A. ¿Qué haces en la casa? Look at the picture. Imagine that you are the person working. Complete each sentence by writing a word from Column A on the first blank, and a word from Column B on the second blank.

Column A
Barro
Lavo
Limpio
Plancho
Quito
Seco

Column B
trapo
lavadora
plancha
secadora
trapeador
escoba

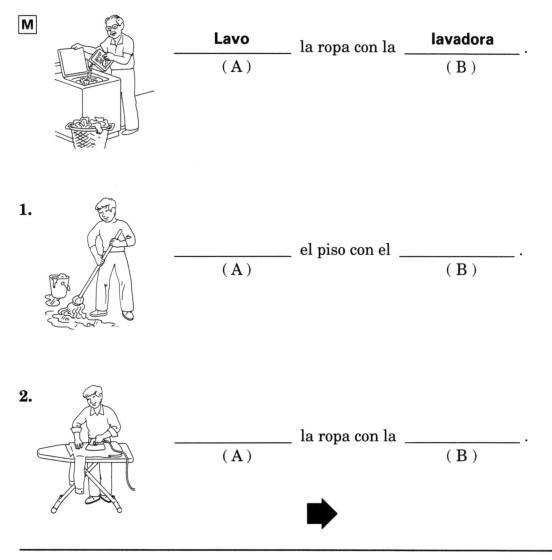

M

__**Lavo**__ la ropa con la __**lavadora**__ .
(A)   (B)

1. _____ el piso con el _____ .
(A)   (B)

2. _____ la ropa con la _____ .
(A)   (B)

Nombre _____

Part **A**, *continued.*

───────────

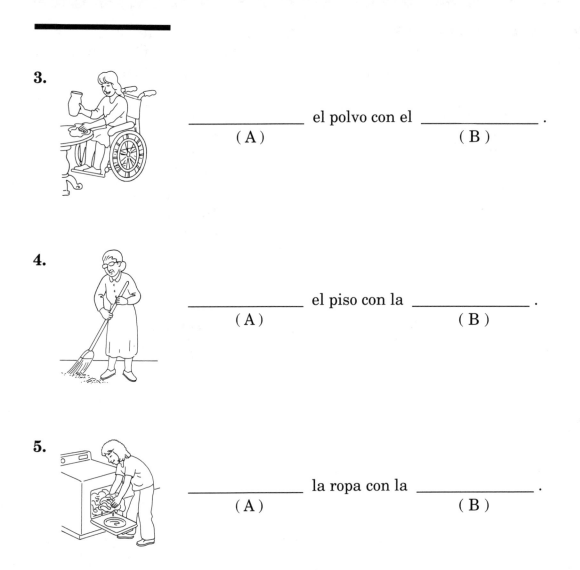

3.

_____ el polvo con el _____ .
(A)   (B)

4.

_____ el piso con la _____ .
(A)   (B)

5.

_____ la ropa con la _____ .
(A)   (B)

Nombre _____

B. **¿Qué vas a hacer?** Read the situation in Column A. Then read what does or does not need to be done in Column B. Draw a line from the situation in Column A to the appropriate statement in Column B. The first two have been done for you.

Column A **Situation**	**Column B** **What does or does not need to be done**
1. Mi ropa está sucia.	Voy a pasar la aspiradora.
2. La alfombra está limpia.	Voy a lavar mi ropa.
3. Tu ropa está limpia.	Voy a quitar el polvo.
4. Hay mucha basura.	Voy a sacar la basura.
5. La alfombra está sucia.	No voy a pasar la aspiradora.
6. Hay mucho polvo en el tocador.	No voy a barrer el piso.
7. El piso está limpio.	No voy a lavar tu ropa.

Nombre _____

Section 2

A. Everyone in the López family shares in the household chores. Complete señora López's sentences to learn what each person has to do. Use the phrases below.

tengo que	tienes que	tiene que	tenemos que	tienen que

M Yo _____**tengo que**_____ regar las plantas.

1. Tú _____ recoger la ropa.

2. Yo _____ lavar la ropa.

3. Tú y yo _____ secar la ropa.

4. Ustedes _____ planchar la ropa.

5. Juana _____ colgar la ropa.

6. Luis _____ barrer el piso.

7. Tú _____ limpiar el piso.

8. Papá _____ pasar la aspiradora.

9. Juana y Luis _____ quitar el polvo.

10. Yo _____ sacar la basura.

Nombre _____

B. In the Gómez family, everyone has just finished doing something enjoyable. Complete señor Gómez's sentences to learn what each family member has just done. Use the phrases below.

---

acabo de   acabas de   acaba de   acabamos de   acaban de

M Ramón **acaba de** _____ mirar la televisión.

1. Rose _____ comer mucho.

2. Tu abuelito _____ comer también.

3. Tú y Ramón _____ nadar.

4. Mamá _____ comprar un vestido.

5. Tú _____ leer un libro.

6. Yo _____ pintar un cuadro.

7. Tú _____ usar la computadora.

8. Ramón _____ recibir una "A".

9. Mamá y yo _____ bailar.

10. Ustedes _____ patinar.

Nombre _____

★ **C.** **¡Muchas tareas y muchos compañeros!** Now, for extra credit, complete the sentences below. Write **con, de,** or **que** on each answer blank. The first one has been done for you.

¡Hola, mamá! Acabo _____**de**_____ estudiar matemáticas _____

Carlos. Ahora tengo _____ estudiar español _____ Elena y

Mirta. Luego, Ana y yo tenemos _____ estudiar ciencias. ¡Caramba!

¡Acaban _____ llegar Elena, Mirta y Ana!

Nombre _____

Section 3

A. Listen to the conversation between a mother, father, son, and daughter. Then you will hear five statements about their conversation. You will hear each statement twice. Circle **CIERTO** if the statement is true. Circle **FALSO** if it is false.

1. CIERTO   FALSO

2. CIERTO   FALSO

3. CIERTO   FALSO

4. CIERTO   FALSO

5. CIERTO   FALSO

B. **Dictado.** Listen carefully to these sentences. You will hear each sentence twice. Write the missing words on the answer blanks.

1. ¿Qué _____ que hacer en tu _____ ?

2. Yo _____ que barrer los _____ .

3. Mi mamá _____ la _____ .

4. _____

5. _____

Nombre _____

★ **C.** Now try writing these sentences for extra credit. You will hear each sentence twice.

1. _____

2. _____

3. _____

4. _____

5. _____

D. Listen carefully to these twelve words. You will hear each word twice. Complete each word by writing **r** or **rr** on the answer blank. The first two have been done for you.

1. ca __r__ o   5. habla _____   9. _____ eloj

2. ca __rr__ o   6. _____ opa   10. a _____ iba

3. pe _____ o   7. saca _____   11. _____ ápido

4. pe _____ o   8. ca _____ ta   12. basu _____ a

Section 1

A. ¡Vamos a poner la mesa! Imagine that you and your friends are setting the table for dinner. First, look at the picture. Then choose a word from the list to complete the sentence.

el azúcar	el mantel	los platos
las servilletas	la crema	la pimienta
la sal	los vasos	las tazas

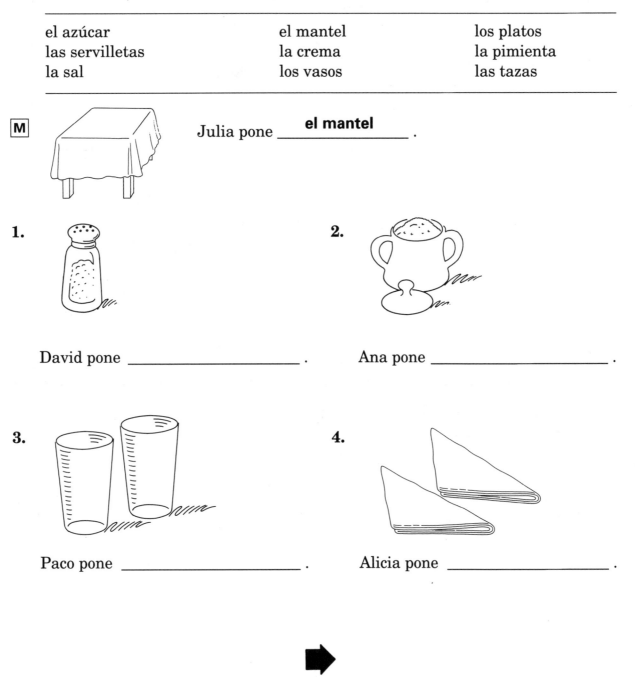

M Julia pone ___**el mantel**___ .

1. David pone _____ .

2. Ana pone _____ .

3. Paco pone _____ .

4. Alicia pone _____ .

Nombre _____

Part **A**, continued.

5.

Carlos pone _____ .

6.

Luisa pone _____ .

7.

Esteban pone _____ .

8.

Sol pone _____ .

B. **Mi fruta favorita.** Tell which fruit each of your friends likes best. First, look at the picture. Then choose the words from the list that complete the sentence.

las cerezas	la piña	la naranja
la sandía	las fresas	las manzanas
los plátanos	las uvas	las peras

M   A Julia le gustan **las fresas** _____ .

Nombre _____

Part **B**, *continued.*

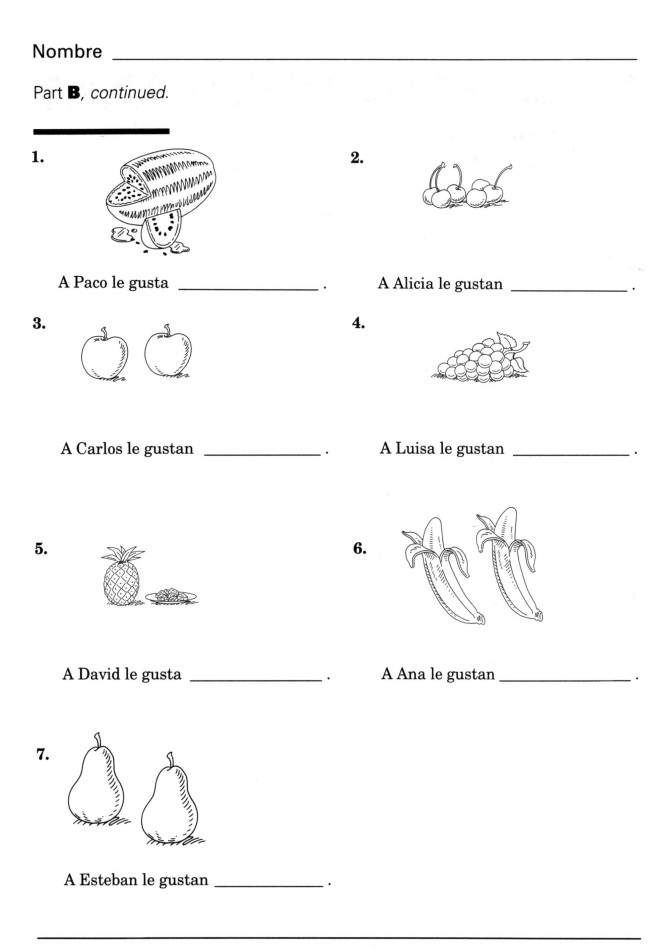

1.

A Paco le gusta _____ .

2.

A Alicia le gustan _____ .

3.

A Carlos le gustan _____ .

4.

A Luisa le gustan _____ .

5.

A David le gusta _____ .

6.

A Ana le gustan _____ .

7.

A Esteban le gustan _____ .

Nombre _____

Section 2

A. ¡Caramba, ya llega! Your mother's boss is coming to dinner. Tell what each person does to help prepare the table. Underline a word to complete each of these sentences.

M Iris (pones / <u>pone</u>) los platos sobre la mesa.

1. Tú y yo (pongo / ponemos) los vasos en la mesa.

2. Ricardo (pongo / pone) las tazas en la mesa.

3. Yo (pongo / pone) la piña en la licuadora.

4. Tú (pones / pone) la sal y la pimienta sobre la mesa.

5. David y Luisa (ponemos / ponen) la crema a las fresas.

6. Tú (pones / pone) el azúcar sobre la mesa.

7. Ustedes (ponemos / ponen) la sandía en un plato.

8. Nosotros (ponen / ponemos) el mantel.

Nombre _____

B. You and your classmates sometimes study together. Complete the sentences telling what each student brings. Use the words below.

| traigo | traes | trae | traemos | traen |

M Carlos _____ **trae** _____ papel.

1. Julia _____ los bolígrafos.

2. Yo _____ los lápices.

3. Tú _____ el borrador para la pizarra.

4. Pepe y Olga _____ los cuadernos.

5. Juan _____ unos libros.

6. Ustedes _____ la tiza.

7. Nosotras _____ platos de papel.

8. Tú y Juan _____ uvas.

9. Catalina _____ manzanas.

Nombre _____

C. Guillermo thinks something is in one place, and Sandra tells him that it's in just the opposite place. Complete Sandra's answers to Guillermo's questions by writing **sobre** or **debajo de (del)** on the blank.

M GUILLERMO: ¿La sandía está debajo de la mesa?

SANDRA: No, está _____ **sobre** _____ la mesa.

1. GUILLERMO: ¿Los libros están sobre la silla?

SANDRA: No, están _____ la silla.

2. GUILLERMO: ¿El vaso está sobre el televisor?

SANDRA: No, está _____ televisor.

3. GUILLERMO: ¿La alfombra está debajo del piso?

¡Claro que no! Está _____ el piso.

★ **D.** **¡Fiesta!** For extra credit, complete this note from Alicia to Anita. On each answer blank write the correct form of the verb in parentheses.

Anita,

Para la fiesta, yo _____ las sillas y tú _____ el
　　　　　　　　　　　(traer)　　　　　　　　　　　　　　　　(traer)

mantel. Alma _____ a sus dos primos. Si tú _____
　　　　　　　　(traer)　　　　　　　　　　　　　　　　　　(poner)

la mesa, yo _____ las flores.
　　　　　　　(poner)

Hasta pronto,

Alicia

Nombre _____

Section 3

A. Listen to the conversation between Cecilia and Juan. Then you will hear five multiple-choice statements about their conversation. You will hear each statement twice. Circle the letter of the phrase that best completes each statement.

1. a   b   c

2. a   b   c

3. a   b   c

4. a   b   c

5. a   b   c

B. Dictado. Listen carefully to these sentences. You will hear each sentence twice. Write the missing words on the answer blanks.

1. Vamos a _____ la _____ .

2. Pepe pone el _____ y la _____ .

3. Amalia pone la _____ y la _____ .

4. _____

5. _____

Nombre _____

★ **C.** Now try writing these sentences for extra credit. You will hear each
sentence twice.

1. _____

2. _____

3. _____

4. _____

5. _____

D. Listen carefully to these twelve words. You will hear each word twice.
Complete each word by writing **s** or **z** on the answer blank. The first two
have been done for you.

1. mú __s__ ica   5. ha _____ ta   9. a _____ ul

2. __z__ apato   6. mar _____ o   10. co _____ a

3. pi _____ arra   7. e _____ cribe   11. bu _____ ón

4. gu _____ to   8. ago _____ to   12. _____ oológico

Nombre _____

Section 1

A. ¡Un desayuno grande! Describe what you eat and drink for breakfast. First, look at the picture. Then choose a word or phrase to complete each sentence.

avena	chocolate	leche	té
café	huevos fritos	mermelada	toronja
cereal	jugo	pan tostado	

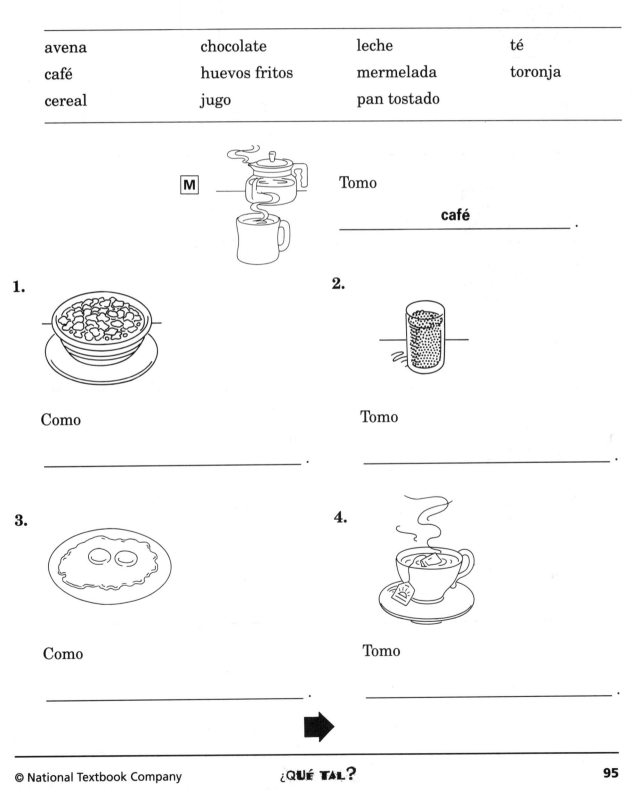

M _____ Tomo

café _____ .

1.

Como

_____ .

2.

Tomo

_____ .

3.

Como

_____ .

4.

Tomo

_____ .

Nombre _____

Part **A**, *continued.*

5.

Como

_____ .

6.

Tomo

_____ .

7.

Como

_____ .

8.

Tomo

_____ .

9.

Como

_____ .

10.

Como

_____ .

Nombre _____

B. Mother has suggestions for a good breakfast. First look at the picture. Then choose a word or phrase from the list to complete each sentence. The first one has been done for you.

beber	querer	huevos revueltos
desayuno	margarina	huevos pasados por agua

1.

Marco, vas a _____querer_____

comer bien mañana.

2.

Celia va a tomar un buen

_____ .

3.

Voy a cocinar unos

_____ .

4.

¿Qué vas a _____ ?

¿Té o chocolate?

5.

Tu papá va comer unos

_____ .

6.

Todo comemos _____

con el pan.

Nombre _____

Section 2

A. Complete the following interview by writing **nuestro, nuestros, nuestra,** or **nuestras** on the answer blanks.

M ¿Son grandes sus ventanas?

No, _____nuestras_____ ventanas son pequeñas.

1. ¿Es pequeño su apartamento?

No, _____ apartamento es grande.

2. ¿Son nuevos sus muebles?

No, _____ muebles son viejos.

3. ¿Es grande su mesa?

No, _____ mesa es pequeña.

4. ¿Son verdes sus cortinas?

No, _____ cortinas son azules.

5. ¿Es azul su alfombra?

No, _____ alfombra es blanca.

Nombre _____

B. Imagine that you are at a restaurant with the García family. Tell what everyone wants to eat. Use the words below to complete the sentences.

| quiero | quieres | quiere | queremos | quieren |

M La señora García _____**quiere**_____ cereal.

1. Yo _____ leche.

2. ¿Tú _____ huevos revueltos?

3. El señor García y yo _____ avena.

4. Pacho _____ toronja.

5. La señora García y Eva _____ chocolate.

6. ¿Ustedes _____ té?

7. Eva _____ jugo de naranja.

8. Nosotros _____ huevos pasados por agua.

9. Pacho y Eva _____ huevos fritos.

10. Sr. García, ¿ _____ usted café?

Nombre _____

C. ¿Nuevo o viejo? Answer each question with the word that means the opposite of the underlined word in the question. Be sure to use the right word endings. The first two have been done for you.

1. ¿Es <u>viejo</u> el espejo?

    No, el espejo es ____**nuevo**____ .

2. ¿Son <u>nuevas</u> las camas?

    No, las camas son ____**viejas**____ .

3. ¿Es <u>nueva</u> la lámpara?

    No, la lámpara es _____ .

4. ¿Son <u>viejos</u> los muebles?

    No, los muebles son _____ .

5. ¿Es <u>vieja</u> la alfombra?

    No, la alfombra es _____ .

6. ¿Son <u>nuevos</u> los radios?

    No, los radios son _____ .

7. ¿Es <u>viejo</u> el teléfono?

    No, el teléfono es _____ .

Nombre _____

★ **D.** Imagine that your friend Ana is showing you photos of her family. Following each of her statements is a comment that you might make. Complete each comment by writing **su, sus, tu,** or **tus** on the answer blank.

[M] ANA: Son mis abuelos.

TÚ: _____**Tus**_____ abuelos son altos.

[M] ANA: Son amigos de mi papá.

TÚ: _____**Sus**_____ amigos son bajos.

1. ANA: Es mi mamá.

   TÚ: _____ mamá es bonita.

2. ANA: Es un amigo de mi papá.

   TÚ: _____ amigo es atlético.

3. ANA: Es mi hermano.

   TÚ: _____ hermano es delgado.

4. ANA: Son mis hermanas.

   TÚ: _____ hermanas son fuertes.

5. ANA: Son amigas de mi mamá.

   TÚ: _____ amigas son altas.

Nombre _____

Section 3

A. Listen to the conversation between David and Hugo. Then you will hear five statements about their conversation. You will hear each statement twice. Circle **CIERTO** if the statement is true. Circle **FALSO** if it is false.

1.   CIERTO   FALSO

2.   CIERTO   FALSO

3.   CIERTO   FALSO

4.   CIERTO   FALSO

5.   CIERTO   FALSO

B. Dictado. Listen carefully to these sentences. You will hear each sentence twice. Write the missing words on the answer blanks.

1. ¿Qué _____ para el _____ ?

2. Yo _____ huevos _____ por agua.

3. Ramona _____   _____ .

4. _____

5. _____

Nombre _____

★ **C.** Now try writing these sentences for extra credit. You will hear each sentence twice.

1. _____

2. _____

3. _____

4. _____

5. _____

D. You will hear a number and a word. If the word has the soft sound of the letter **c** in it, circle the number. If the word does not have the soft **c**, do not circle the number. The first three have been done for you.

(1.) (centro)	4.	7.	10.	13.
(2.) (cinco)	5.	8.	11.	
3. (cuatro)	6.	9.	12.	

Nombre _____

Section 1

A. Read the words in the list. Then look at each picture below. On the answer blank, write the word that completes the sentence under the picture. The first one has been done for you.

jugo	secar	té
sacar	servilleta	tenedor

1.

Voy a tomar

_____ **jugo** _____ .

2.

El _____
está sobre la mesa.

3.

¿Usted toma

_____ ?

4.

Es una _____
blanca.

5.

Tiene que _____
la ropa.

6.

Tiene que _____
la basura.

Nombre _____

B. Look at the picture. Then write a word on the answer blank to complete the sentence. The first one has been done for you.

1.

Barre el piso con la

_____ **escoba** _____ .

2.

Jaime usa la

_____ .

3.

¿No te gustan las

_____ ?

4.

¿Te gustan las

_____ ?

5.

Siempre comemos huevos

_____ .

6.

Voy a comer

_____ .

Nombre _____

Section 2

A. Complete the conversation between Sara and her mother. On the answer blank, write the correct form of the verb in parentheses. The first one has been done for you.

SARA: Mamá, yo ___**acabo**___ de recibir una "D" en ciencias.
(acabar)

MAMÁ: Sara, tú _____ que estudiar más.
(tener)

SARA: Pero, mamá, yo _____ mis libros a casa todos los días…
(traer)

MAMÁ: Yo comprendo, Sara. Mañana tú y yo _____ el reloj
(poner)

para las seis de la mañana. Tu hermano también _____

estudiar temprano.   (querer)

B. **¿Dónde está el gato?** Use the words below to complete the conversation. The first one has been done for you. Some words may be used more than once.

| con | de | en | debajo de | que | sobre |

JUAN: ¿El gato acaba ___**de**___ salir?

INÉS: No, el gato tiene _____ estar _____ la casa.

JUAN: ¿El gato está _____ Ana?

INÉS: No, Ana no está _____ la casa.

JUAN: ¿El gato está _____ la mesa?

INÉS: No. ¡El gato está en el piso, _____ la mesa!

Nombre _____

C. Complete the answers to these questions about belongings. Use words from the list.

mi	su	nuestros
tu	nuestro	nuestras

M ¿Es grande tu cuarto?

No, _____**mi**_____ cuarto es pequeño.

1. ¿Está aquí el amigo de Luis?

No, _____ amigo no está aquí.

2. Juan, ¿vas a mi casa?

Sí, voy a _____ casa.

3. ¿El perro de ustedes es grande?

No, _____ perro es pequeño.

4. ¿Los amigos de ustedes son simpáticos?

Sí, _____ amigos son simpáticos.

5. ¿Las hijas de ustedes viven en casa?

Sí, _____ hijas viven en casa.

REPASO: UNIDADES 7-9 / EXAMEN

Nombre _____

Section 3

A. Listen to the conversation between Rubén and Rita. Then you will hear five multiple-choice statements about their conversation. Circle the letter of the phrase that best completes each statement.

1. a b c

2. a b c

3. a b c

4. a b c

5. a b c

B. Dictado. Listen carefully to these sentences. You will hear each sentence twice. Write the missing words on the answer blanks.

1. ¿ _____ está _____ perrito?

2. Está _____ de la _____ .

3. _____ perrito _____ que comer.

4. _____

5. _____

Nombre _____

C. Listen carefully to these twelve words. You will hear each word twice. Complete each word by writing the missing letter on the answer blank. The first two have been done for you.

1. pe __r__ a

2. __s__ ofá

3. pe _____ o

4. _____ apato

5. _____ erca

6. _____ adio

7. ta _____ a

8. _____ ereal

9. pa _____ ados

10. po _____ que

11. ve _____ es

12. co _____ e

Nombre _____

Section 1

A. Imagine that you are in a restaurant and are naming the foods your friends want. First, look at the picture. Then choose a word to complete the sentence. The first one has been done for you.

hamburguesa	pan	pollo
legumbres	papas	queso

1.

Rita quiere

pan .

2.

Diego quiere

_____ .

3.

Susana quiere

_____ .

4.

Luis quiere

_____ .

5.

Teresa quiere

_____ .

6.

Gerardo quiere una

_____ .

Nombre _____

B. Tell what each person likes for dinner. First, look at the picture. Then choose the words that complete each sentence and write them on the answer blank.

el arroz	los guisantes	el maíz	el pescado
la carne	el jamón	el pavo	las zanahorias

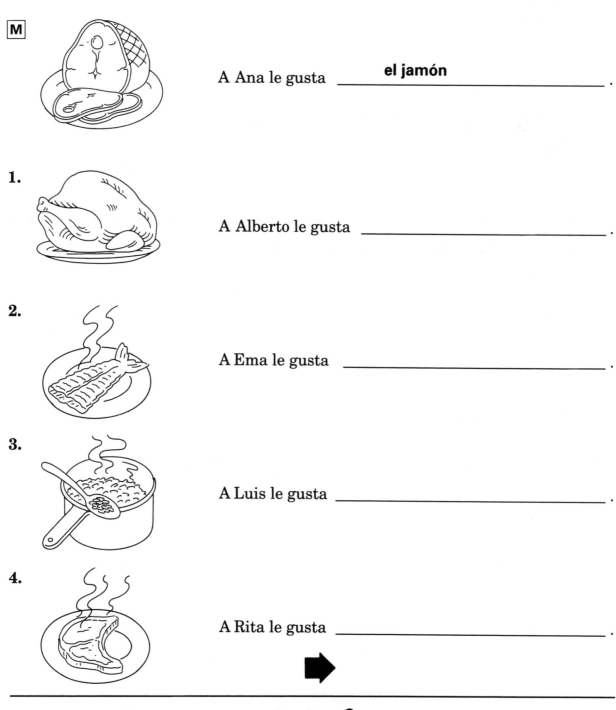

M A Ana le gusta _____**el jamón**_____ .

1. A Alberto le gusta _____ .

2. A Ema le gusta _____ .

3. A Luis le gusta _____ .

4. A Rita le gusta _____ .

➡

Nombre _____

Part **B**, continued.

5.

A Víctor le gustan _____ .

6.

A Inés le gustan _____ .

C. Use the words below to complete the conversation between Luis and Ana.
The first one has been done for you.

almorzar	comer	gustar	poder	probar

LUIS: Ana, es mediodía. ¿Quieres _____**comer**_____ ?

ANA: No, gracias. No quiero _____ ahora.

LUIS: Vamos, Ana. ¿Quieres _____ el jugo de zanahoria? A ti te

va a _____ mucho.

ANA: Ahora no puedo. ¿Vas a _____ tomar la cena en mi casa
esta noche?

LUIS: Sí. Puedo ir a tu casa a las ocho.

Nombre _____

Section 2

A. Nuestro almuerzo. Complete these sentences to tell where or with whom these people have lunch. Use the words below.

almuerzo	almuerzas	almuerza	almorzamos	almuerzan

[M] Silvia _____**almuerza**_____ con sus padres.

1. Yo siempre _____ a las once y media.

2. Sra. López, ¿usted _____ en la escuela?

3. Mis abuelos _____ en casa.

4. Rosa, ¿dónde _____ tú?

5. Los sábados Ana _____ muy temprano.

6. Luis y yo _____ con nuestros compañeros.

7. Nosotros siempre _____ al mediodía.

8. Alicia y Antonio _____ a las dos de la tarde.

Nombre _____

B. **¿Te gusta?** You and your friend are talking about what foods you like and dislike. Use the words below to complete the sentences. The first two have been done for you.

mí	él	nosotras	ellas
ti	nosotros	ellos	ustedes

1. A _____mí_____ me gusta la gelatina.

2. A _____ellos_____ les gusta el pescado.
   (a los niños)

3. A _____ les gustan las hamburguesas.
   (a Ana y a Eva)

4. ¿A _____ les gustan los espaguetis?
   (a ti y a David)

5. A _____ no me gusta la ensalada.

6. A _____ no le gusta el café.
   (a Roberto)

7. A _____ no les gusta el té.
   (a Juanita y a Carla)

8. A _____ no nos gustan los mangos.

9. ¿A _____ no te gustan los huevos revueltos?

Nombre _____

C. **La cena.** Use the words in the list to complete the conversation between Ramona and Enrique. Some words may be used more than once. The first one has been done for you.

puedo	puedes	puede	podemos	pueden

RAMONA: Enrique, ¿ ___**puedes**___ almorzar conmigo?

ENRIQUE: Lo siento, Ramona, no _____ . Tengo que estudiar con Ricardo.

RAMONA: Bueno. ¿Entonces tú _____ cenar con mi familia esta noche? Mi papá cocina muy bien.

ENRIQUE: Hmm. ¿Ricardo también _____ ir?

RAMONA: ¡Cómo no! Todos _____ cenar. ¿A qué hora

_____ ustedes estar en mi casa?

ENRIQUE: ¿A las siete en punto?

RAMONA: De acuerdo. Hasta luego, Enrique.

Nombre _____

★ **D.**   Now, for extra credit, fill in the blanks to complete this conversation
between Pepe and his mother.

MAMÁ: Pepe, ¿a _____ te gusta el arroz?

PEPE: No, mamá, no _____ gusta.

MAMÁ: ¿Te _____ las papas?

PEPE: No, mamá.

MAMÁ: Entonces, Pepe, ¿qué _____ gusta?

PEPE: Mamá, yo soy como Popeye. ¡A _____ me gustan las
espinacas!

Nombre _____

Section 3

A. Listen to the conversation between Mirta and Eduardo. Then you will hear five multiple-choice statements about their conversation. You will hear each statement twice. Circle the letter of the phrase that best completes each statement.

1. a   b   c

2. a   b   c

3. a   b   c

4. a   b   c

5. a   b   c

B. Dictado. Listen carefully to these sentences. You will hear each sentence twice. Write the missing words on the answer blanks.

1. Para el _____ quiero un _____ .

2. Bueno. _____ uno de _____ .

3. ¿Hay _____ de _____ ?

4. _____

5. _____

Nombre _____

★ **C.** Now try writing these sentences for extra credit. You will hear each
sentence twice.

1. _____

2. _____

3. _____

4. _____

5. _____

D. Listen carefully to the following words. You will hear each word twice. If
you hear the hard sound of the consonant **c** in a word, circle **sí**. If you do not
hear the hard sound of **c**, circle **no**. The first two have been done for you.

1.	(sí)	no	5.	sí	no	9.	sí	no
2.	sí	(no)	6.	sí	no	10.	sí	no
3.	sí	no	7.	sí	no	11.	sí	no
4.	sí	no	8.	sí	no	12.	sí	no

Section 1

A. Tell what Alicia and Gregorio have to do each day. First, look at the picture. Then choose a word from the list that names the action in the picture. Write the word on the answer blank. The first one has been done for you.

acostarse	despertarse	levantarse	quitarse
bañarse	irse	peinarse	secarse
cepillarse	lavarse	ponerse	volver

Por la mañana, Alicia tiene que…

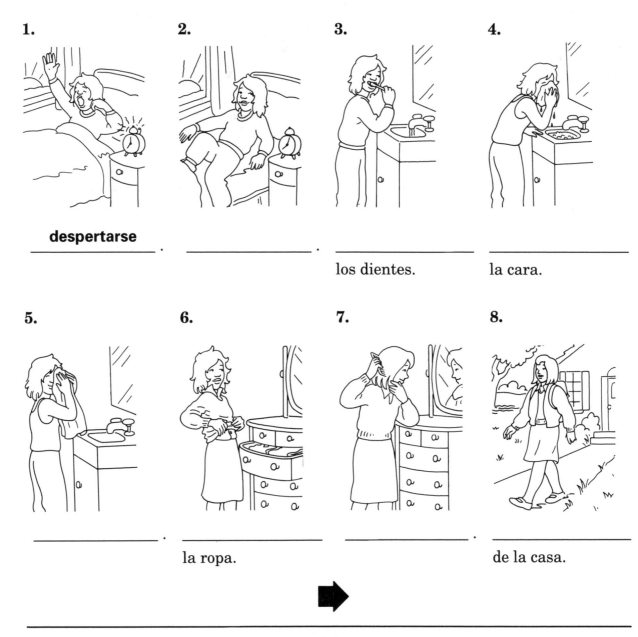

1.

despertarse .

2.

_____ .

3.

_____
los dientes.

4.

_____
la cara.

5.

_____ .

6.

_____
la ropa.

7.

_____ .

8.

_____
de la casa.

Nombre _____

Part **A**, *continued.*

Por la noche, Gregorio tiene que…

9.   **10.**   **11.**   **12.**

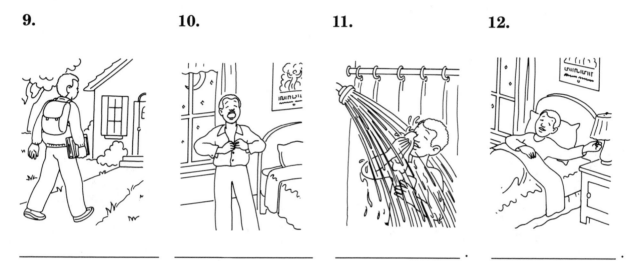

_____   _____   _____ .   _____ .

a la casa.   la ropa.

Nombre _____

B. First, read the sentence. If the actions are in the right order, write **bien.** If they are not, rewrite the sentence, changing the order. The first two have been done for you.

1. Primero me pongo el pijama y luego me acuesto.

   bien
   _____

2. Primero me levanto y luego me despierto.

   Primero me despierto y luego me levanto.
   _____

3. Primero me baño y luego me quito la ropa.

   _____

4. Primero me despierto y luego me cepillo los dientes.

   _____

5. Primero me baño y luego me peino.

   _____

6. Primero me seco y luego me lavo la cara.

   _____

Nombre _____

Section 2

A. Tell about the Ortega family's daily activities. Underline the words that correctly complete each sentence below.

M   Luisa (se levantan, <u>se levanta</u>) a las siete.

1. Raúl (me lavo, se lava) la cara.

2. Yo (me baño, se baña) primero.

3. Luego, Raúl y yo (me cepillo, nos cepillamos) los dientes.

4. Por último, mamá y Lucía (se peina, se peinan).

5. ¿Tú no (se baña, te bañas) por la mañana?

6. David (nos levantamos, se levanta) temprano.

7. Tú siempre (te acuestas, se acuesta) tarde.

8. Juan y Teodoro (se ponen, nos ponemos) los zapatos rápido.

9. Ana y yo (nos despertamos, me despierto) a las seis.

10. Yo no (me acuesto, te acuestas) temprano.

Nombre _____

B. **¡Pensamos hacer muchas cosas!** Tell what you and your friends are thinking of doing this weekend. Choose the word that completes each sentence.

| pienso | piensas | piensa | pensamos | piensan |

M   Roberto _____**piensa**_____ ir a nadar.

1. Yo _____ leer un poco.

2. Sra. Torres, ¿usted _____ ir a las tiendas?

3. Rafael y Martina _____ bailar.

4. Miguel, ¿ _____ volver a la casa temprano?

5. Graciela _____ estudiar.

6. Paquita y yo _____ mirar la televisión.

7. Ana, ¿tú _____ comprar ropa?

8. Rosario y Francisco _____ limpiar la casa.

9. Nosotros _____ comer en el patio.

10. Yo _____ practicar los deportes.

Nombre _____

★ **C.** **¿Qué me pongo?** Ana is thinking about the clothing she will wear to the basketball game. For extra credit, complete her thoughts by writing **me,** **nos,** or **se** on the answer blanks.

_____ vamos a las siete. Yo _____ pongo el vestido azul.

Como va a hacer frío, _____ pongo el abrigo. Catalina

_____ pone una falda verde. María y Alicia _____ ponen

pantalones.

Nombre _____

Section 3

A. Listen to the conversation between Alicia, Gregorio, and their mother. Then you will hear five multiple-choice statements about their conversation. You will hear each statement twice. Circle the letter of the phrase that best completes each statement.

1. a   b   c

2. a   b   c

3. a   b   c

4. a   b   c

5. a   b   c

B. Dictado. Listen carefully to these sentences. You will hear each sentence twice. Write the missing words on the answer blanks.

1. _____ la mañana _____ temprano.

2. _____   _____ de la casa.

3. Las clases _____ a las _____ .

4. _____

5. _____

Nombre _____

★ **C.** Now try writing these sentences for extra credit. You will hear each sentence twice.

1. _____

2. _____

3. _____

4. _____

5. _____

D. You will hear a number and a word. If the word has the sound of the letter **q** in it, circle the number. If the word does not have the sound of **q**, do not circle the number. The first two have been done for you.

(1.) (queso)	4.	7.	10.
2. (garaje)	5.	8.	11.
3.	6.	9.	12.

Nombre _____

Section 1

A. **¿Dónde trabajan?** Draw a line from the worker to the workplace. The first one has been done for you.

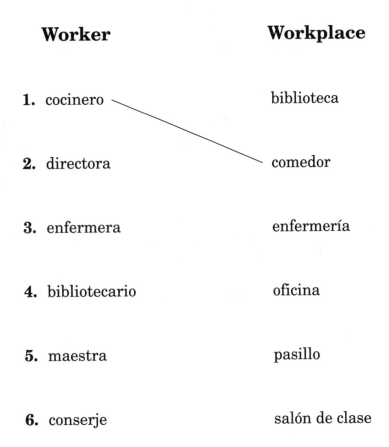

Worker	**Workplace**
1. cocinero	biblioteca
2. directora	comedor
3. enfermera	enfermería
4. bibliotecario	oficina
5. maestra	pasillo
6. conserje	salón de clase

Nombre _____

B. **¿Cuál es su trabajo?** Look at the person in the picture. Then find the word that names the person's job and write it on the answer blank. The first one has been done for you.

bibliotecaria	conserje	enfermera
cocinero	director	maestra

1.

Sr. Herrera

director

_____

2.

Sra. Chávez

_____

3.

Sr. Cervantes

_____

4.

Sra. Sierra

_____

5.

Sra. Fuentes

_____

6.

Sr. Durango

_____

Nombre _____

C. Look at the picture. Then use a word or phrase from the list to complete the sentence about the picture. The first one has been done for you.

bajar	salida	auditorio
fuente de agua	subir	entrada

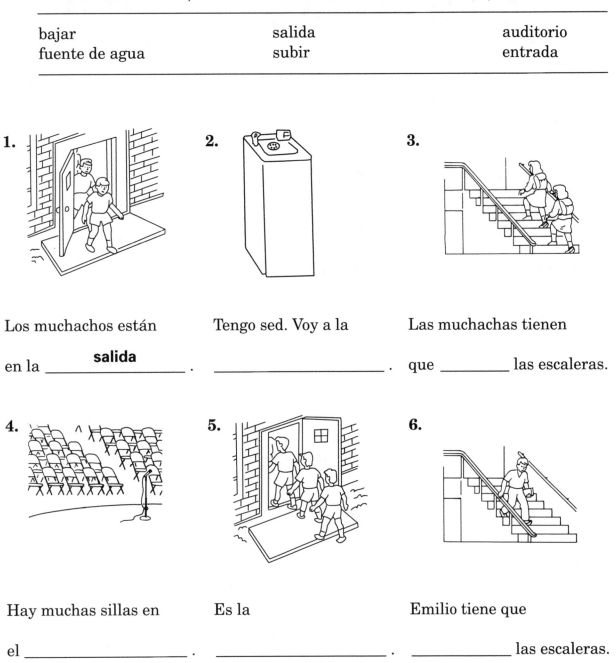

1.

Los muchachos están

en la __**salida**__ .

2.

Tengo sed. Voy a la

_____ .

3.

Las muchachas tienen

que _____ las escaleras.

4.

Hay muchas sillas en

el _____ .

5.

Es la

_____ .

6.

Emilio tiene que

_____ las escaleras.

Nombre _____

Section 2

A. ¡Gente inteligente! Tell what skills these people have. Complete each sentence with the appropriate form of **saber.**

| sé | sabes | sabe | sabemos | saben |

M Inés _____**sabe**_____ hablar español.

1. Yo _____ usar la computadora.

2. Sr. Durango, ¿usted _____ cantar?

3. Luis y yo _____ escribir en español.

4. Julia, ¿tú _____ bailar?

5. Carlos y Elena _____ nadar.

6. Nosotros _____ cocinar.

7. Víctor _____ usar la lavadora.

Nombre _____

B. Read the pairs of sentences below. Pay special attention to the underlined word in the first sentence of each pair. On the answer blank, write the word which has the opposite meaning of the underlined word.

M El suéter es <u>nuevo.</u>

El suéter es _____**viejo**_____ .

1. <u>Siempre</u> hablo con Anita.

    _____ hablo con Anita.

2. <u>Alguien</u> está en la casa.

    _____ está en la casa.

3. Hay <u>algo</u> en el piso.

    No hay _____ en el piso.

4. Voy a <u>subir</u> las escaleras.

    Voy a _____ las escaleras.

5. ¿Dónde está la <u>entrada</u> del auditorio?

    ¿Dónde está la _____ del auditorio?

Nombre _____

C. Look at the lines **(líneas)** and squares **(cuadrados).** Then read the statements under them. Circle **sí** if the statement is true. Circle **no** if it is false.

A ——————————————

B ————————————————————————

C ——————————————————————————————————

| M | Línea **C** es más larga que Línea **B.** | (sí) | no |

1. Línea **B** es más larga que Línea **A.** sí no

2. Línea **A** es menos larga que Línea **B.** sí no

3. Línea **B** es más larga que Línea **C.** sí no

4. Línea **C** es la más larga. sí no

¿QUÉ TAL?

Nombre _____

Part **C**, *continued.*

A

B

C

D

M Cuadrado **D** es el más grande.   sí   (no)

5. Cuadrado **A** es el más grande.   sí   no

6. Cuadrados **C** y **D** son los menos grandes.   sí   no

7. Cuadrado **B** es más grande que Cuadrado **A**.   sí   no

8. Cuadrado **A** es menos grande que Cuadrado **B**.   sí   no

★ **D.** Paloma and her family are all tall. For extra credit, complete this description of them by writing **alto, altos, alta,** or **altas** on the answer blanks.

Paloma es muy _____ .

¿Es _____ su hermana?

Sí, Paloma y su hermana son _____ , pero su papá es más

_____ que ellas.

Todos son muy _____ .

    ¿QUÉ TAL?

Nombre _____

Section 3

A. Listen to the conversation between Estela and Javier. Then you will hear five statements about their conversation. You will hear each statement twice. Circle **CIERTO** if the statement is true. Circle **FALSO** if it is false.

1.   CIERTO   FALSO

2.   CIERTO   FALSO

3.   CIERTO   FALSO

4.   CIERTO   FALSO

5.   CIERTO   FALSO

B.   Dictado. Listen carefully to these sentences. You will hear each sentence twice. Write the missing words on the answer blanks.

1. El Sr. López _____ en la _____ .

2. ¿ _____ hace _____ ?

3. _____ hacer de _____ .

4. _____

5. _____

Nombre _____

★ **C.** Now try writing these sentences for extra credit. You will hear each sentence twice.

1. _____

2. _____

3. _____

4. _____

5. _____

D. Listen carefully to these twelve words. You will hear each word twice. If you hear the consonant **g** in a word, circle **sí**. If you do not hear the consonant **g**, circle **no**. The first two have been done for you.

1. (sí)   no   5. sí   no   9. sí   no

2. sí   (no)   6. sí   no   10. sí   no

3. sí   no   7. sí   no   11. sí   no

4. sí   no   8. sí   no   12. sí   no

Nombre _____

Section 1

A. Read the sentences below. Then look at the pictures. On the answer blank under each picture, write the letter of the sentence that matches the picture. The first one has been done for you.

a. El buzón está delante de la casa.

b. Hay un ropero en mi dormitorio.

c. La lámpara es nueva.

d. Es un cuchillo.

e. Tenemos una batidora eléctrica.

f. El abrelatas está en la cocina.

1.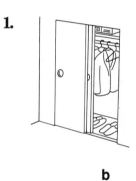

b
_____

2.

_____

3.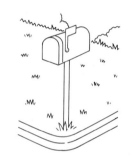

_____

4.

_____

5.

_____

6.

_____

Nombre _____

B. First look at the picture. Then choose the word that completes the sentence about the picture. Write the word on the answer blank. The first one has been done for you.

| huevos | regar | toronja |
| pan | pone | zanahorias |

1.

Son _____ **zanahorias** _____ .

2.

Me gustan los _____
revueltos.

3.

Hay _____ .

4.

No me gusta la _____ .

5.

Sandra se _____ la
ropa.

6.

Rosa tiene que _____
las plantas.

Nombre _____

C. Look at each picture. Then, on the answer blank, write the word that completes the sentence about the picture. The first one has been done for you.

1.

A Rosa le duele la ___**cabeza**___ .

2.

No hay _____ en el plato.

3.

A Diego le queda _____ la camisa.

Nombre _____

Part **C**, *continued.*

_____

4.

Diana no es alta. Ella es _____ .

5.

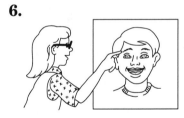

Quiero compar el _____ bonito.

6.

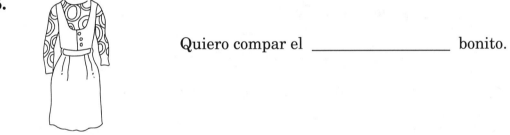

Rebeca toca la _____ .

END-OF-YEAR TEST

Nombre _____

Section 2

A. Complete these sentences, using the words below. The first one has been done for you.

ellos	mí	sus
les	se	tu

M Aquí está _____**tu**_____ papá.

1. A ellas _____ gusta cantar.

2. A _____ no me gustan los gatos.

3. Rosita es alta, pero _____ padres son más altos.

4. Alicia _____ despierta a las seis y media.

5. Roberto y Luis son amigos; _____ almuerzan a la una.

B. Complete the sentences below. Write the correct form of each verb in parentheses.

M Pablo _____**habla**_____ poco.
   (hablar)

1. Carlos siempre _____ las legumbres.
   (probar)

2. Ella _____ patinar muy bien.
   (poder)

3. Los maestros _____ ir al auditorio.
   (pensar)

¿QUÉ TAL?

Nombre _____

Part **B**, *continued.*

━━━━━━━━━━

4. Tú _____ los dientes primero.
(cepillarse)

5. Yo _____ nadar muy bien.
(saber)

6. ¿Alicia y tú _____ pintar la casa?
(querer)

7. David siempre _____ la mesa.
(poner)

8. Usted _____ que comer más.
(tener)

9. Ellas _____ pantalones.
(usar)

10. Nosotros _____ las puertas temprano.
(abrir)

11. ¿Dónde _____ ustedes?
(estar)

12. Ellos _____ mis abuelos.
(ser)

13. Inés y Luisa _____ en mi casa.
(almorzar)

14. A los muchachos les _____ los tobillos.
(doler)

15. A Fernando le _____ mal las botas.
(quedar)

Nombre _____

Section 3

A. Listen to the conversation between Jaime and Sonia. Then you will hear five multiple-choice statements about their conversation. Circle the letter of the phrase that best completes each statement.

1. a   b   c   **4.** a   b   c

2. a   b   c   **5.** a   b   c

3. a   b   c

B. Dictado. Listen carefully to these sentences. You will hear each sentence twice. Write the missing words on the answer blanks.

1. ¿Cuando _____ a _____ ?

2. _____ a las _____ .

3. _____

4. _____

5. _____

C. Listen carefully to these twelve words. You will hear each word twice. Complete each word by writing a vowel or consonant letter on the answer blank. The first two have been done for you.

1. m __e__ s   5. e _____ ero   9. cere _____ a

2. __s__ ala   6. a _____ ajo   10. _____ ubia

3. a _____ ora   7. niñ _____   11. _____ erra

4. h _____ jo   8. _____ uerido   12. do _____ a